P9-CPZ-671

Education and Freedom

This book is dedicated to America's children, who all—each and every one of them—need and deserve the best possible education.

Education and Freedom

By H. G. RICKOVER
Vice Admiral, USN

Foreword by EDWARD R. MURROW

Preface by CHARLES VAN DOREN

E. P. DUTTON & CO., INC.
New York, 1959

Washington still has two kinds of office buildings, the roomy modern kind worthy of a great capital and those thrown up as emergency quarters during the war, which by now are dingy and slumlike. In a rundown two-story back-alley building, well behind Constitution Avenue, is housed a staff of men who have done, and are doing, one of the extraordinary jobs of modern times. They planned and built the *Nautilus*, the first central station power plant at Shippingport, Pa., and are creating our nuclear navy. These are the offices of Vice Admiral Hyman G. Rickover and his men.

Admiral Rickover loves to do battle with lethargy and barnacled tradition. To get results he will tear up any conventional procedures. It has not made him popular with Washington bureaucracies that his results have been sensational, and no one can deny that the Navy and the Atomic Energy Commission, under which he serves, have not shown much pride in him.

I first met Admiral Rickover in the course of doing a television program called "Revolution in the Navy." This involved porpoising about for three days in the *Nautilus*, shooting an interview with Admiral Arleigh Burke on the *Forrestal*, visiting the missile cruiser *Boston*, the submarine *Albacore*, and various shore installations. Near the end of the filming I went to Washington to interview Admiral Rickover, and began putting the usual questions about nuclear power and weapons and their effect on naval strategy and thinking. Early in the interview Admiral Rickover interrupted my questioning to say: "Why don't you ask questions about the really important things?" He then went on to say that education is the most important problem that faces us today. "It is even more important than atomic power in the Navy," he said, "for if our people are not properly educated in accordance with the terrific requirements of this rapidly spiraling scientific and industrial civilization, we are bound to go down. The Russians," he added, "apparently have recognized this."

Admiral Rickover is no theoretical pedagogue. His attitude toward American education was the result of practical experience, and it is worth all the more for that very reason. He found the inadequacy of our schools when he recruited his staff. With the opening of the atomic era he himself went in for an intensive education in nuclear physics and engineering, and inspired his closest associates to join him. Then, when he was assigned to build the first nuclear power plant for naval use, he had to create a working force of highly educated specialists. They had to be like himself, know what the nuclear age meant, be willing to make sacrifices to equip themselves for it, and understand that utterly new engineering standards were called for. He discovered that such men were hard to come by. American education was not supplying them tailor-made for the exacting new duties.

Since his initial discovery he has devoted every available moment to education, and has now become our foremost advocate of an educational system that meets the challenge of the atomic era. He has spoken forcefully and frequently on this theme, and this book, largely based on these speeches, is in my opinion the most stimulating and searching analysis of the perils of inadequate preparation for the nuclear age that I have encountered.

More than any man I know, Admiral Rickover respects nothing but ability. Rank, wealth, position mean nothing to him. The only thing he fears is that the ship of state will founder as the result of an excess cargo of ignorance and from the rust and barnacles of indifference and the waste of man power and natural resources. He works incredibly hard. He demands and receives the same kind of work from his staff. He will occasionally admit that he is pleased with the performance of some individual or piece of hardware, but as far as I know he has never confessed to being satisfied.

He once said to me in an interview: "One thing that possibly deludes us is the current belief that we can do everything better than anybody else in the world. We have a tendency to do quite a bit of bragging. Other people are just as good as we are. I have seen no patent from the Lord saying that Americans are better than anyone else or have more brains than anyone else. We do have more wealth than other people. We have a greater opportunity to become better than other people. But I am not sure we are taking advantage of that opportunity as much as we could."

Here is a remarkable book, packed with salient facts, dictated from experience and inspired by wisdom. Admiral Rickover is more than a naval officer who pushed through a crash program of building nuclear power plants. He is greater than that. He is a prophet and a leader. He says that we must train better scientists and technicians, but also more responsible men. He has no specialist's contempt for the humanities. Basically what he wants is to see intelligence and the disciplined mind become respectable. He knows that only if they do will we have a chance to hold our own in the demanding years before us.

EDWARD R. MURROW

Oh that mine adversary had written a book! cried Job in his affliction, and ever since the wisest men have known, as God did on that occasion, that it is better not to. Particularly a book on such a thorny subject as modern education. Thorny and difficult it certainly is; no subject is more prone at this time to prejudice and parochialism. For Admiral Rickover it would have been safer to remain silent. Yet he has not done so. His courage receives my admiration and gratitude.

The first reaction of many Americans to Admiral Rickover's temerity will be to ask what right he has, since he is not a professional educator, to write of education. This is a common attitude, though not I think a just one. We are inclined to leave speculation to experts; every man has his area of competence, within which his opinions are absolute, outside of which he is supposed to be a nincompoop. We no longer have a high regard for amateurs in anything, forgetting that the amateur, etymologically at least, has love on his side—a quality perhaps even more important than skill and experience. In the present case love is evident on every page. Admiral Rickover loves man and his works and his possibilities; he therefore cares for education (caring for is the basis of all true love). Indeed, he cares so much for man and that which allows him to be most manly—that is, education—that he sometimes becomes truculent. Not in this book, though; it is an articulate and sensible work. There is no truculence here. The book reveals the author's deep concern for his species and his country. That is all; but that is sufficiently rare.

It is of course not quite fair to imply that Admiral Rickover is an amateur. Among other things, his book discusses the educational programs the author has instigated in the course

8

of designing and building the first atomic ships, and the first central station atomic power plant at Shippingport, Pennsylvania. The men who must make and man them, the Admiral discovered, could not be prepared for the task by any existing educational system; he therefore invented a system. This is typical of the way Admiral Rickover goes about things. He had of course to be an iconoclast, and iconoclasts are never revered by the idolators involved. Iconoclasts are nevertheless terribly necessary; particularly, as the Admiral points out more than once, in democracies. In fact, democracy ceases without them. This is an aspect of his courage for which we must be thankful.

Admiral Rickover is courageous in another sense. He is not afraid to learn from others—friends as well as enemies (it is sometimes harder to learn from friends). He discusses Russian education and points out that the best parts of it are copied from the European educational system. I think he overestimates Russian education. It is not nearly so good in general, nor so effective in the production of good scientists and engineers, as we have been led to believe. But if he is in error here, it matters very little. It is better to overestimate than to underestimate Russian education. Most important, it is good to remember that we can improve ours by thinking about theirs. Admiral Rickover is willing to try new methods and attitudes wherever found. He is an educated man; he knows, that is, that his education has only just begun.

We in the West, we who are so tremendously fortunate as to live in democracies (not yet entirely just ones), must in the coming era fight for their lives as well as for our own. We will lose both our lives and our freedom if we do not care enough about education. Particularly we will lose if we forget that education demands faith. We must believe in the educated man; we must give our students everything we have, and trust them to use what we give them as they see fit, not as we see fit. We must be willing to let the chips fall where they may. We cannot ordain the future; above all we cannot assume that it will be like the present. I suspect the real trouble with Russian education is that it makes just this error. Admiral Rickover does not make it. As I said, he loves man and believes in his infinite possibilities—educated man's, that is.

This is a fine and thoughtful book, and it is probably going to make a lot of people very angry. I think that's a good thing.

CHARLES VAN DOREN

ERRATA

1. *page 33, line 2 from bottom, should read:* That very egg-head is considered . . .
2. *page 71, line 7, should read:* No longer can anyone take all knowledge . . .
3. *page 79, line 18, should read:* . . . engineer has an effect on our . . .
4. *page 82, line 8, should read:* 94 per cent. Five sixths of all the . . .
5. *page 112, line 19, should read after the word* emphasis: that is put upon things of the mind. Some children are raised in an atmosphere of respect for learning . . .
6. *page 165, line 7, should read:* . . . they allowed maximum intellectual freedom.
7. *page 209, line 15, should read:* . . . ratio of teachers to pupils—one for every twelve students.

CONTENTS

The greater part of the material in Chapters 1-9 is based on speeches given by the author on the following occasions: December 11, 1958, The Harvard Club of New York City, New York, New York; January 12, 1956, The Society of Business Magazine Editors, Washington, D. C.; March 11, 1957, Westinghouse Science Talent Search Award Ceremony, Washington, D. C.; May 14, 1957, Annual Scientific Assembly of the Minnesota State Medical Association, St. Paul, Minnesota; September 25, 1958, Engineers Club of St. Louis, St. Louis, Missouri; November 20, 1956, The Institute sponsored by The Thomas Alva Edison Foundation, Inc., East Orange, New Jersey; March 23, 1958, the sesquicentennial of St. Albans School, Washington, D. C.; April 19, 1958, the inauguration ceremonies of Polytechnic Institute of Brooklyn, Brooklyn, New York; November 22, 1957, The Institute sponsored by the Thomas Alva Edison Foundation, Inc., at the Engineering Society of Detroit, Detroit, Michigan.

Education and Freedom

*"If a nation expects to be ignorant and free,
in a state of civilization, it expects what
never was and never will be."*

Thomas Jefferson

Chapter 1

EDUCATION IS
OUR FIRST LINE OF DEFENSE
—MAKE IT STRONG

Copyright © 1958 by H. G. Rickover

This book is a collection of speeches made during the last four years. Some have been shortened, others expanded, and some new material has been added to produce an orderly sequence. There is no Aristotelian unity in it but each chapter touches on some aspect of education and freedom. Each, whether or not it deals with education directly, points up the need of better schooling for all our children—education far superior to anything we in this country have ever had or ever needed in the past. Only massive upgrading of the scholastic standards of our schools will guarantee the future prosperity and freedom of the Republic.

This is a conclusion which I reached as a result of my personal experience with developing a new source of power —nuclear fission. Engaged in research, development, and building of nuclear power plants as the Atomic Energy Commission and the Navy are, we found that this could not be done unless we raised our thinking and our actions to technological levels well above those prevailing at the time. This in itself is difficult. It means that everyone concerned with designing reactors must be more broadly and more thoroughly educated than the average engineer. But this is not all. Since our reactors were not mere laboratory models but were expected to propel ships and supply energy to central-station power plants, many people outside my own group were drawn into the work and we needed the cooperation of industrial and governmental organizations. The categorical imperative of atomic energy demanded that those who were involved in the building of reactors also had to raise their thinking and their actions to higher levels of

competence. In particular, what was needed was an upgrading of administrative procedures and of standards of
accuracy in industrial production. It is no exaggeration to
say that a major part of our time was taken up with fighting
for higher levels of performance which were resisted because
their necessity was not understood. We had great difficulty
convincing outsiders that more rigorous standards were
essential if nuclear power was to be harnessed safely and
efficiently. This resistance arose from what one might call
an intellectual toryism—an inflexibility that may have its
roots in an educational system which does not prepare
young people for life in a constantly changing world, subject to recurrent *bouleversements* which rapidly make old
attitudes and procedures obsolescent and demand that all
our leaders have flexible and versatile minds. In one sense,
this book represents my groping for an answer why so many
road blocks, technical and nontechnical, delayed building a
nuclear navy as fast as I consider essential to the security
of the country. In a broader sense, the conclusions I reached
apply to delays hindering *all* attempts at technological
break-throughs; they seek to pin point the elements which
hinder all new development projects, whether in jet engines,
rockets, missiles, satellites, or in the efforts to obtain energy
from hydrogen fusion.

Because of limitations of time and of acceptable book size,
the body of the book concentrates on what I consider the
major obstacle—the inadequacy of the American educational
system in this dynamic twentieth century. I have touched
lightly in this chapter on what I consider the most vexing
nontechnical problems—the inability of our institutions to
find a place for the creative expert and their persistence in
believing that novel projects can be carried through by routine methods. Fuller treatment of this problem must be post-
poned to a future date.

Whenever man makes a major advance in his age-old
effort to utilize the forces of nature, he must simultaneously
raise his education, his techniques, and his institutions to a
higher plateau. Let me illustrate this by giving an example

of a past upgrading necessitated by a shift from one energy source to another.

If you obtain your power from human muscle, wind, or water, you need almost no technical knowledge. To drive a gang of galley slaves, to manage a windmill or water mill do not even require literacy, but putting Faraday's invention of the dynamo to practical use in a central-station power plant needed fifty years of engineering effort by highly trained people. The men who run such plants use their minds a great deal more and they need much better minds than the quondam miller or slave driver. Similarly, from the splitting of the atom in the 1930's to the bomb in the 1940's, to the practical nuclear power plant in 1953, a vast amount of intellectual effort of a high order had to be expended. Highly trained nuclear engineers are needed to design, build, and run nuclear power plants. Still greater demands on the human mind will be made if and when we obtain energy from hydrogen fusion.

It is obvious that the kind of American who thoroughly mastered his environment on the frontier in the muscle, wind, and water state of technology would be totally ineffective in the atomic age which is just around the corner, and the fusion age which is still a way off. Social workers in big cities into which people from our last-frontier regions have been pouring are fully aware of the inadequacy of these human beings in an urban environment for which their simpler life had not prepared them.

The consequence of technological progress is that man must use his mind more and his body less. We still think in terms of a more primitive era; we overvalue physical prowess and undervalue intellectual competence. This has a profound effect on our attitudes toward education. The kind of school which prepares young people adequately for life in a less complicated environment is of little use today. Nor do we need schools that concentrate primarily on adjusting the children of immigrants to this new country; on helping them become Americans quickly and painlessly. Today we must have schools which develop in all children—talented, average, and below average—the highest level of intellectual competence of which they are capable; schools that help young people to understand the complex world of today and how it came to be what it is. This means that our schools must return to the traditional task of formal education in Western civilization—transmission of the nation's cultural heritage, and preparation for life through rigorous training of young minds to think clearly, logically, and independently.

For as long as I have worked in the atomic-energy field I have been absorbed in educational problems. Indeed, I found the two so intertwined that I would have had to be most unobservant not to have gotten myself involved with American education. When I started on the work of harnessing the energy of the atom for propulsion of naval ships and generation of electricity in civilian power plants, I had in my group a handful of men with training in nuclear engineering. We knew that our project would present difficult technical problems, particularly since I deemed it necessary to speed the work by telescoping the usual pattern of development which proceeds from theoretical to applied research, to laboratory experimentation, and finally to practical application. We designed and built reactors directly for practical use in ships and power plants, skipping the stage when theory is tried out on laboratory models. To the layman—and alas even more so to the public-relations man—such models always seem to be equivalent to the working, finished product. This is not so. This country has many laboratory reactors—reactors producing some electricity under ideal laboratory conditions, and much is to be learned from them. There is a vast difference, however, between a research or experimental reactor and a reactor which must actually produce useful power for a ship or an electric grid. Whereas laboratory conditions favor the new project, reality is troublesome.

When I set up my reactor group twelve years ago, I put all my energy into finding the right people and wasted no time creating an "ideal" organization. In fact we still have no formal organization. We have excellent people, carefully chosen, thoroughly trained for their job, and strongly motivated because of their intense interest in the work. Such people cannot be fitted into the usual hierarchic organization which exists in most industrial and government complexes. They must be given freedom to work out their own problems and to assume responsibility for what they do. They need an environment that allows them to be venturesome and does not stifle their initiative with routines; in a novel development project there can be no routine.

Our country will not be able to make rapid technological progress unless we reorganize our institutions. These must be pried from their exaggerated veneration for routine and protocol and made to see that provison must be made for both routine work and for new and creative work; for routine workers and for people with specialized knowledge who must be allowed to operate outside routine procedures. We have not yet solved this problem; chiefly, I believe, because it is relatively new, a consequence of two new phenomena—the scientific revolution and organizational growth necessitated by population expansion.

The scientific revolution now engulfs us though not all of us are fully aware of this. We must expect that science will influence our mores in ever increasing degree. There will be some unemployment in the ranks of people whose principal qualification is their ability to get along, to fit into organizational structures, and to adjust. The man of the future on whom we shall depend more and more is the technical expert. Today he is still subservient to nontechnical leaders in government and industry, and his work is hampered and sometimes destroyed by men in whom is vested great power but who cannot understand the realities of the new, artificial, technological age. But the "verbal" men are on the way out; the men who can handle the intricate mysteries of complex scientific and engineering projects are on the way in. That applies all along the line down to the skilled workman on whose judgment, concentrated attention, and responsibility may depend the functioning of some new and gigantic piece of engineering. To put this in military terms: we shall need more technical sergeants and fewer martinets. In our naval nuclear program we have taken cognizance of this demand for a different kind of man and we have set up schools to train the officers and men who will run the new atomic navy.

Another relatively new phenomenon in American life which compels us to find room for creative people in our institutions is the sheer mass of our people. Government and industry must in some manner organize and manage our huge population to prevent chaos and insure safety and efficiency. No other industrial democracy has to cope with a problem of quite such staggering dimensions for none is so populous or grows at such dizzying speed as we do.

Our founding fathers knew that size endangers democratic institutions and they had some misgivings as to whether democracy would function in as populous a country as ours. In the mid-eighteenth century, when plans for an independent America began to ripen, we *had 1.2 million people*—exactly twice the population of the only then existing democracy, Switzerland. All other democracies had been small city-states—Plato's republic was to have had 5,040 citizens! Where Switzerland had quadrupled its population in two hundred years, we *increased more than a hundredfold*. We can be proud of our record of maintaining democratic processes, even expanding them, despite this enormous increase in population. While we have been highly successful politically, economically there has of necessity been a gradual loss of personal freedom. Each year fewer people are self-employed; more become submerged in huge organizations. In fact, nothing grows faster than organization. Increasing specialization aggravates this trend. Even professional people have been losing independence and increasingly work as members of a team. Without organizations run by competent administrators we simply could not get along. This presents few problems if the work is routine. A capable administrator can learn enough about the techniques of routine production or service to organize it efficiently; he knows how to oil the machinery and dovetail individual work into the whole. The people under him do not know more than he about the essentials of the routine procedures in which they are engaged.

It is entirely different with experts having specialized knowledge. Few administrators know enough about the work of subordinate experts to be competent to administer or manage them efficiently. Most administrators reach their positions in the organizational hierarchy because they understand routine personnel problems, know how to keep people working contentedly, and are always subservient to the wishes of their superiors. The typical administrator is used to "group-think" in committees—whether brainstorming or ordinary—and has limited his own originality so severely that he has no understanding of the freedom essential to the creative worker. His mental processes are the very opposite of those of the expert, especially the scientist or engineer. Men whose minds have been trained to respect intellectual honesty and scientific fact simply cannot submit to the orders of administrative superiors whose intellectual honesty they may not respect and whose "scientific facts" they may regard as fable. *There is no hierarchy in matters of the mind.*

This causes a great deal of friction. What appears to the organization man as an almost criminal insubordination is to the trained professional a vital necessity; unless he is allowed to follow his own judgment in matters pertaining to his specialty, he becomes a hack. His intellectual freedom is so intimate a part of his nature that to yield to a superior lacking technical knowledge is to degrade himself and become unfree. Actually, administrators can contribute very little that is useful to the work of creative people. In fact, nobody can waste as much time as a super-efficient administrator trying to run a group of "eggheads."

I fear that we have gone far toward lowering the output of our brainworkers by overorganizing them. We are drowning in paper work. We are talking ourselves into a standstill in endless committees—those pets of the administrator. We are losing the genius we once had for improvisation. Now-

adays nothing can be done without elaborate preparation,
organization, and careful rehearsal. We have been diluting
responsibility for making decisions by piling layers of super-
visory administrative levels, pyramid fashion, upon the people who do the real work. All this delays new developments.
To the technical difficulties of creating something new are
added the constant frustrations of interference by men who
do not understand technical matters. If we are to regain
ground lost to the Russians in important developments, we
must learn how to run organizations with sufficient flexibil-
ity so that routine work may proceed efficiently without
interfering with creative work. Somehow every organization
must make room for inner-directed, obstreperous, creative
people; sworn enemies of routine and the *status quo*, always
ready to upset the applecart by thinking up new and better
ways of doing things. They are troublesome mavericks, un-
loved by the administrator who cannot forgive their contempt for conventions. However, unless these people are
permitted to lead the way, there will be stagnation.

It was men of independent mind and venturesome spirit
that I set out to find for my nuclear propulsion group. From
the start it was evident that no experienced men of this type
were available. Before we could tackle our work, we therefore had to find young people showing *potentialities* of
growth whom we could then ourselves train intensively for
work on reactor design. This took time, but in the end it has
proved far more satisfactory than the usual custom of raid-
ing the small hoards of already qualified people accumu-
lated by other government agencies or industries. We set up
special schools and turned ourselves into teachers, discover-
ing in the process that the fundamentals of a good liberal-
arts education had been skimped in the education given
these bright young men. The search for and training of
promising young people still take up much of my time and
that of my leading engineers for we are constantly expanding and there are of course losses through attrition. These,
fortunately, are few so that we reap pretty much of a full
harvest from our educational efforts.

Among the young engineers we interview we find few who have received thorough training in engineering fundamentals or principles; but most have absorbed quantities of facts—much easier to learn than principles but of little use without application of principles. Once a principle has been acquired it becomes a part of one and is never lost. It can be applied to novel problems and does not become obsolete as do all facts in a changing society. American education in general emphasizes learning factual know-how at the cost of absorbing fundamental principles, just as it stresses conditioning of behavior at the cost of developing the ability to think independently. Most of our schools have lost sight of the fact that a well-trained mind can cope with many unforeseen problems. Instead, they try to foresee every possible future difficulty a young person may encounter and then give a special course in how to deal with it. This is a hopeless endeavor, for in a rapidly changing world no one can foresee what future problems will have to be met.

I have interviewed more than two thousand young men in the last twelve years. My naval-reactor engineering group presently numbers about one hundred fifty. Since the men I interviewed had already passed through a number of previous interviews which weeded out all but the best, it can be seen that those who could not meet the requirements of the nuclear-power project—and hence inferentially of *any* new development project—vastly outnumbered those who qualified.

This experience made a deep impression on me. It led me directly to a study of why our educational system produces so few men who are qualified to do the work which we must do if we are to progress. Our schools are the greatest "cultural lag" we have today. When I read official publications put out by the men who run our educational system—booklets such as *Life-Adjustment Education for Every Youth* or *Education for All Youth*—I have the strange feeling of reading about another world, a world long since departed if it ever existed at all. I sense the kindly spirit, the desire to make every child happy, the earnest determination to give advice on every problem any young person might ever meet in life—and withal so complete a misunderstanding of the needs of young people in today's world that it frightens me. If I speak out against this mistaken concept of what twentieth-century American education must be, I do so out of no desire to find fault with those who misread the demands of the times but from anxiety for the future of our children. I am worried about the chances which young people, so poorly equipped to deal with modern life, will have when things become more complex and difficult, as they surely will before very long.

Today's big problems for young people are not how to choose the proper tie, or how to be socially popular—these are minor problems which any mother can teach her children with little difficulty. They are piddling problems. The important problems our young people will have to meet in life cannot be foreseen; the only way to prepare for them is to make sure that all our children will be truly "educated." By that I do not mean the same thing as some of our educationists. Witness the statement of a teachers' college dean, quoted in John Keats' revealing book *Schools Without Scholars:* "An educated man is one who is well adjusted and helpful in his community." When the dean was asked "whether a man who was well adjusted and helpful could be considered educated *without also being able to count his fingers or write his name,*" the dean said, "Yes."

Apart from the life-adjustment fallacy so prevalent among American educationists, our schools seem unable to concentrate on training young minds because of partiality for so-called "useful" knowledge. This utilitarian concept of education is to be found among parents no less than among educationists. It may be in the nature of a revolt against liberal-arts education which many consider suited only for gentlemen of leisure and hence out of place in a democracy. An extraordinary lot of nonsense is said and believed about European education which stresses the liberal arts. European education is dismissed as aristocratic and exclusive, perhaps in order to avoid having to stand the test of comparison which might necessitate eventual upgrading of American education. Unfortunately, constant repetition that ours is the only democratic and universal education has been lulling and persuasive. It has been so effective that we have the oddest delusions about academic life abroad. In American folklore the European student becomes a golden youth in blazers and white flannels, living in ivy-clad seclusion amid shady campuses while the vast majority of young people are sternly excluded from this higher education. This is an unreal concept of European university life as it is today and as it has been in the past. Far from being islands of aristocratic privilege, European universities have always been intellectual workshops of austere aspect. In the long and honorable history of learning which sets Western civilization apart from all others and to which the Western world owes its dynamic quality, the scholar and the student have more often been poor than rich. The medieval and renaissance universities which shaped the crude intellect of Europe through association with the polished mind of Greece and Rome offered no more nor less than a chance to seek truth —to achieve liberation of the mind from ignorance and superstition.

These universities were built of men—professors and students—rather than of brick and mortar. Lacking fixed assets, they went wherever academic freedom could be found. In truth, that was all they needed. Unencumbered by material possessions, Europe's students were free to wander from university to university, searching for the best professor in their field of study. Traditionally, scholars have been as rich in spiritual freedom as they have been poor in tangible wealth.

This point is illustrated by a story concerning Guarino, a famed Italian of the fifteenth century who taught rhetoric and Greek in a small Italian town. Students flocked to his classes from the four corners of Europe. In coldest weather they waited patiently outside the room in which he lectured —shivering in their thin garments, undeterred by freezing rain or snow. Such actions would be considered extremely

odd today. Guarino spent most of his income helping the
poorest of his students, and with them he lived in great
poverty. Still, one must not think that life was grim. Medieval students were as full of pranks as are today's. Guarino
himself was a sociable soul. He often invited his friends to
share with him *fave e favole*—beans and conversation!

True enough, professors and students formed a cosmo-
politan elite, but it was an elite of the mind, not one of
social privilege. Communicating with each other in the universal language of scholarship—Latin, steeped in a common
heritage of classical Greek and Roman culture—the scholars
were the first true Europeans. Upon the unity of spirit and
mind which they built must rest today's hope for unification
of that divided continent. All of us in the West owe to them
our phenomenal wealth and power—all of us benefited when
the trained minds of scholars took on the task of putting
science to work on man's age-old problems of disease and
want. And it is by liberal-arts curricula that their minds
were trained, not by life-adjustment education or vocational
training.

Europe is a mere spot on the map of the world; a crowded,
poorly endowed peninsula of the vast Asian heartland. Even
today, mortally wounded by two fratricidal wars, this small
continent possesses wealth and influence all out of proportion to its size and natural endowment. Until the outbreak
of World War I she was more powerful than all non-Euro-
pean countries combined. Her economic and political power
has always rested on her supremacy in matters of the mind,
especially in the sciences. Formal public education, public
libraries, universities, highly trained "professions" with
rigorous ethical codes—all these are European inventions.
All arise from sharpening of the human intellect, from widespread recognition that knowledge is an end in itself; that a
cultivated mind changes the quality of life and lifts it to a
higher level and, by doing so, creates happiness.

In his book *The Idea of a University* John Henry Newman
gives us one of the best definitions of a liberal education. He
says that "it brings the mind into form." Once so formed,

the intellect has a connected view or grasp of things; "it will display its powers with more or less effect according to its particular quality and capacity in the individual." To him, as to all Europeans, a liberal education was not reserved to the talented but something which could also help the average man to grow in wisdom. "In all," wrote Newman, "it will be a faculty of entering with comparative ease into any subject of thought, and of taking up with aptitude any science and profession." Of the uneducated he says that a "haziness of intellectual vision is their malady. . . . They think that any one truth excludes another which is distinct from it and that every opinion is contrary to their own opinion which is not included in it . . . nothing which meets them carries them forward or backward, to any idea beyond itself. . . . Everything stands by itself, and comes and goes in its turn, like the shifting scenes of a show, which leaves the spectator where he was."

No plaything for the idle gentleman is this liberal-arts education based on the humanities and the sciences. It makes little sense for us to go on refusing to profit from Europe's educational experiences. By even the most pragmatic of tests her education has proved itself. Consider that in but one single branch of learning—theoretical physics— Europe has produced some fifteen to twenty men of high originality in the last one hundred years. The United States, writes Lancelot Law Whyte, produced "only one: J. Willard Gibbs (1839–1903), the great physical chemist, a lonely figure who did not found a school." Much of our superior standard of living has been owing more to the fact that we applied European techniques to a vast, fabulously rich land than to any superiority of Americans in competence, determination, industry, or education. It is only now, when Russia has begun to apply European techniques to her own vast land, that we are meeting competition on equal terms.

We have of course done exceedingly well with our natural riches; we can be proud of what we have accomplished. But, unless we understand the important part played by America, the land, in our enviable life, we shall not be able to keep

moving forward as fast as we did in the past, for our land
now has far fewer natural resources and far more people.
In just half a century we have changed from an exporter to
an importer of many vitally needed raw materials. Daily we
become more dependent on other countries for the sinews
of our economic and military power. We are deficient in
eighteen of the thirty most important industrial minerals
and we lack five completely; our oil production will pass its
peak about 1965, twenty years before this happens in the
world at large. Then we shall have to import oil or undertake the costly process of utilizing shale-oil deposits. It is
possible that we may then have to operate with energy
which is more expensive than that used elsewhere. This will
adversely affect our standard of living and our political
power. Imperceptibly some of the foundations supporting
our present prosperity and world position have been getting
weaker. As always happens when things are turned upside
down, it takes a while for people to readjust their beliefs to
changed conditions.

Most Americans still think of ours as an empty, fabulously
rich country and of our people as superior to all others, if
not in everything at least in everything technical. Yet, a
healthy baby born today may well live to see a population
density in this country as high as that of Europe, excluding
Russia. We have much semi-arid and eroded land; Europe
has no semi-arid regions and she has preserved her soil, her
forests, and her water supply. We lost almost 3 per cent of
our most fertile farm lands in fifteen short years (17 million
acres), but small Holland has been wresting a whole new
province from the North Atlantic. Charles Morrow Wilson
estimates that the acreage in roadsides of the United States,
not including other rights of way, is equal to the size of
the state of Georgia, the largest state east of the Mississippi.
Our rapid urbanization alone destroys annually one million acres of land which will never again produce a crop.
Much of it was good farm land. In the past we could afford
to be wasteful but in the future we may have to follow
Europe's example and condemn only the poorest land for

housing or factory development. The day may come when future Americans will even deplore our fine new interstate highway system which will cost us 2 million acres of land.

The use a people makes of its natural resources is basically a matter of education and wisdom. We have not done so well as Europe in this matter. We still think there are no limits to expansion in this country, even though the warning signals are here for all to see. Our wastage of water alone will soon bring us up against a really serious problem. Last year distilled water was sold in Dallas, Texas, at fifty cents a gallon!

There is but one way out of our worsening raw-materials position and that is to develop to their utmost our human resources—the minds of our young people. They will need far more highly trained minds than the ones we get by with in order to cope with the poorer and more crowded world we are bequeathing to them. One of the ways in which we can ease their problems is to provide ahead of time for eventual replacement of natural resources by artificial, man-made substitutes such as atomic energy, which may to some extent replace fossil fuels when these are finally exhausted. Every day we waste in fighting those who interfere with development of substitutes for the irreplaceable resources we ourselves are using up will hurt future Americans. For the sake of our descendants, we must get on with this work and not let ourselves be stopped or slowed by outdated attitudes, institutions, or hallowed procedures.

Our present educational system does not produce enough trained people to carry forward new projects of this kind. We would be wise to investigate how Europe educates her children, for she prepares them better than we do for the more difficult life we must expect in the future. Yet she maintains a decent and comfortable standard of living on her very limited resources and her crowded land. It is not too early to prepare for a time when our children must be as well equipped as Europe's because our future is her present.

We often personalize countries when we want to make a

point. Countries do act through human beings and analogies therefore have some validity. To paraphrase Donne, no country is an island, entire of itself. We are not so great and wise that we cannot profit from the experience of others, especially from countries that have lived longer than we and that have had some measure of success. We are nearly all of us children of Europe. Like young people the world over, younger countries go through a phase when they reject everything the parent country stands for, believes in, and does. But we are growing older. Has not the time come when we can associate with Europe as grown-up children do with their parents? I am reminded of what Mark Twain said:

"When I was a boy of fourteen, my father was so ignorant I could hardly stand to have the old man around. But when I got to be twenty-one, I was astonished at how much the old man had learned in seven years."

Never rich in land or raw materials, Europe achieved enormous power, prosperity, and world influence through cultivation of brain power. It seems advisable to me that we observe how she did this.

We can learn from her respect for the superior human mind—the kind of mind we need to move our techniques to higher levels and thus to offset loss of tangible national wealth. For the first time in history the mind is really coming into its own. Only countries which understand and respect the creative processes of the intellect will be able to maintain themselves in decency in this over-full world. Only those who give free scope to men who work creatively will progress. It is strange that the importance of intellectual freedom and creativity should have been better understood in authoritarian Prussia and totalitarian Russia—bent on exploiting human intelligence for the benefit of power-hungry rulers—than in our own humane democracy. Prussia and imperial Germany were pioneers in establishing an excellent public educational system, adequate for the masses and highly conducive to development of superior scientific achievement by the talented few. It was so good that many European democracies adapted it to their own needs. Russia has now adopted our ideal of universal education and combined it with the excellence of the European educational system, and in but twenty-five years she has worked wonders. We do not want her school system. We must devise one suited to our own needs. In it we, too, must combine the ideals of universal education and of scholastic excellence.

At different levels of civilization, different degrees of popular education are needed. A future dependent on creative brains obviously must have an educational system quite different from the one needed when men of brawn and physical courage exploited this continent. With hindsight we now see the mistakes of the past; we realize that we would now have better soil, cleaner rivers, and more extensive forests had there been some infusion of informed thinking, some consideration of future needs when our natural wealth was expropriated during the great westward movement. Past Americans have mined our incredibly rich soil, ravaged our forest, and squandered our mineral and fuel resources with reckless, with truly heroic abandon. Future Americans will have to make shift with less natural wealth. They will manage this if we prepare them for greater intellectual exertion by providing a vastly better educational system.

Our schools have done a fine job making Americans out of motley groups of foreigners from all corners of the globe and doing it in record time. This job is finished. The schools must now tackle a different job. They must concentrate on bringing the intellectual powers of each child to the highest possible level. Even the average child now needs almost as good an education as the average middle- and upper-class child used to get in the college-preparatory schools. The talented child needs special schooling to move him rapidly through the period of absorbing knowledge into the period when his fine mind can turn this knowledge into new ideas, new discoveries, new ways of life. We need creative thinkers in the humanities no less than in the sciences. Living in crowded areas demands more of us in tolerance, in consideration, and in acceptance of necessary rules than life on a frontier. Perhaps our children—certainly our grandchildren—

will have to live with fewer material possessions. It is not too early to turn to inner resources which are limitless: to art, music, literature, good conversation; to cultivation of a more contemplative way of life.

Democracy is a growing force. It never reaches perfection. It ever finds new objectives. To achieve it in a small, homogeneous farming community is one thing. To maintain it in a metropolitan, highly industrialized country is another. We must not make shibboleths of words such as "democracy" and "equality." I think that Erich Fromm gave us a wonderful definition for both. In an interview with Mike Wallace he said that democracy is consent by the governed, active participation and responsibility of each citizen in the whole social life; not being a little cog who is satisfied that he is manipulated the right way, by persuasion and not by force. But I like his definition of equality best. It means, he said, that we are all created in the image of God, and "that no man must be the means for the ends of another, that every man is an end in himself." That, he said, "is the only equality there is."

This democracy and this equality do not require that we deny to the minority of people with creative minds the right to use them in their own way and to their fullest potential. They do not mean that we cannot accept the rare contributions which creative people are able to make merely because not everybody can do the same thing. Nor should the great ideas of democracy and equality be vulgarized into exaction of conformity to the opinions and tastes of the majority on pain of being considered odd, undemocratic, stuck up, or maladjusted. People who use their minds successfully ought not to be expected to pretend they are just like everybody else—except, of course, for the one matter in which they excel. We have gone quite far in forcing unusual people to buy acceptance from us by making a show of their simple tastes, their conformity to popular views of what constitutes a "normal" person. It is often by this form of crude flattery alone that they win permission to do their work. The people rule and they rule as absolutely as the Bourbon kings of

France. France was not run very well when everyone had to win the king's permission for necessary actions by flattering him. Then, too, the most effective flattery was imitation. Nothing the king did was too silly or trivial not to be immediately copied by every ambitious courtier.

Here celebrities of one kind or another must all win the people's permission to be themselves by similar imitation. It is seldom enough that a woman is both beautiful and a gifted actress. To keep her public happy she must also make a great show of domestic virtues—perhaps feign to like scrubbing her kitchen floor. It isn't enough for a brilliant scientist to have made a discovery which will bring great benefit to millions of average people; he must also pretend that he shares all the endearing little foibles and simple pleasures of the average man. Everyone who is in any way unusual suffers from the arrogance of mediocre people. I have before me a résumé of a "research" project undertaken by certain educationists in which they set themselves up as judges of the character and personality of scientists of note. What strikes these judges is the alleged poor social adjustment of these unusual people, and one is made to feel that this defect far outweighs any possible contributions the scientists may have made to the common good. Recently an eminent scholar made some pertinent observations about American life. At least one commentator chose to report on this solely in terms of the color and shape of the scholar's socks. A small amount of respect and tolerance would lessen the estrangement now existing between the "eggheads" and the public at large. Last year Viscount Hailsham proposed a toast to the Royal Society in which he talked back at some of these detractors of intelligence. Many an American "egghead" must have felt like cheering. "Eggheads of the world, unite!" urged the viscount. "We have nothing to lose but our brains. A country neglects its eggheads at its peril. For it is the egghead who is the greatest realist. It is the egghead who invents the Sputnik, not the captain of the football team." That every egghead is considered "unfit for the society of successful politicians, hardheaded men of business,

simple soldiers, silent sailors or working journalists, and all
the other kind of folk who make such a botch of this practical world by refusing to think about the theoretical problems involved in the art of living."

We might get some very practical results if we tried to
understand our brainworkers better; if we stopped thinking
of science as a mere "comfort-grinding machine," a term
coined by Huxley in a moment of anger; if we respected the
true scientist's thirst for knowledge for the sake of knowledge and his irritation when we keep asking "will it be useful
for us"?

We are now in a somewhat chastened mood and we pay
some attention to the constant urging that we respect intellectual work, and value those who earn their livelihood by
using their brains. But what is needed is really a very simple, very human act on our part: acceptance of the diversity
of man and of every man's right to be himself. Natural endowments are unevenly distributed and it is unrealistic to
ask that a brilliant person also be personable and charming
and that he enjoy watching the fights on TV. A dedicated
scientist is no less a "whole person" if chitchat bores him
and he gets more excited over the color change in a test tube
than over the most colorful gadget his neighbor has just
bought. He may irritate people because the things the average person considers important, he thinks unimportant.
Communication between scientists and ordinary people is
difficult. But can't they respect each other from a distance?
It may well be that the ad men's *beau ideal,* the gray-
flanneled young executive with the ulcers and the exurban
home who has nary an original idea in his head but is blessed
with lots of charm and knows all the angles—it could just
be that he is *less* "well adjusted" than the absent-minded
professor.

In Victorian times the general public would not forgive
its greatest artists their often somewhat disorderly love life,
forgetting that it was balanced by the divine spark of their
creativity. We have outgrown this infantile Puritanism. In
fact, we now enjoy reading of the hectic emotional escapades

of even minor Hollywood celebrities and charitably feel that such things have to be expected of stars. This is because everyone can understand and enjoy the special talents of these people. Few of us, however, can understand what can be produced for our benefit by the intensely concentrated thinking of introverted brilliant men. We ought to learn to be tolerant of their different patterns of life and take it on faith that nothing great is ever created without such intensity of concentration.

My regular work goes on seven days a week leaving me very little leisure time. Moreover, I am neither a writer nor an orator. I should, therefore, not have spoken out if the obstacles to progress merely delayed the time when we can profit by the benefits of higher technical competence. What induced me to voice my concern was the threat of Russia which, as any engineer would, I noticed many years ago when the first bad news came trickling from behind the iron curtain—bad news of astonishing scientific and engineering achievements; of a revolutionary reform in Russian education; of Russian success in combining mass education with highest-quality education for large numbers of her children. Most disturbing to me was the clear evidence that we were losing momentum at the very moment when Russia was increasing hers. This could be seen in the delays besetting all our new developments of military hardware; in our worsening lead time. This is the term applied to the time that elapses between conception of an idea and the finished product incorporating this new idea. Our lead time on military items, which was two and a half years during World War II, has now lengthened to ten years. Meanwhile, Russia's lead time has steadily shortened and is now five years. This particular consequence of interference with technological progress really started me in earnest on speech making. I consider this lengthening lead time extremely dangerous for our survival as a free nation. It was difficult, before Sputnik, to present the full picture of Russian successes in the realm of the intellect. There was little patience then in this country with anyone who told of areas where

we were no longer supreme. Unpleasant facts were so un-
welcome that it was actually risky to mention them.

We were not quite so impatient of the critic as the ancient
Locrians, mentioned in J. S. Mill in his *On Liberty*.[1] These
people undoubtedly felt that they gave freedom of speech to
all citizens though at a cost which many must have considered too high. At public meetings anyone could stand up and
argue for changes in law or custom, on one condition. A rope
was placed around his neck before he began to speak and
if what he said did not meet with public approval, he was
forthwith hanged. This, no doubt, prevented the frivolous
and the crank from disturbing the even tenor of familiar
customs and ways of life.

As a people we have always frowned on the critic of social
mores, particularly when he voiced criticism of the manner
in which certain groups of people earn a living. De Tocque-
ville remarked in 1831 that he knew of no country in which
there was so little freedom of discussion as in America, and
he comes back again and again to what seems to him an
inexplicable phenomenon in a free domocracy—"freedom of
opinion does not exist in America." Many thoughtful Americans have also observed this with concern. John Jay Chapman, post-Civil War essayist and critic, deplores our
unwillingness to debate freely when someone's business or
professional interest is involved and gives numerous examples; one, the case of Harriet Martineau, English novelist
and economist, who found herself socially boycotted in Boston in the 1830's because, so she was later told, "I had
avowed, *in reply to urgent questions,* that I . . . condemned
the institution of slavery. . . . The subservience to opinion
at that time," she remarks, "seemed a sort of mania." It is
curious that this should have happened in Boston where
abolitionist sentiment was widespread at that time. But, so
Chapman explains, the society of Beacon Hill, having inti-

[1] I owe this reminder to an excellent article pleading for courageous
criticism published in a new magazine—*Modern Times*—by W. T. Couch
and entitled, "The Word and the Rope."

mate business relations with southern cotton planters, "could not afford to have values disturbed."

Our timidity in the face of organized pressure tactics by groups whose interest it is to silence all comment on matters they wish to order to their own satisfaction, without regard to the possibility that this may do damage to the nation as a whole—this timidity continues to this very day. Robert M. Hutchins warns us that we must realize that "an uncriticized culture cannot long endure." It would indeed be tragic if democracy deteriorated into mass tyranny over the unconventional individual. We should then lose the diversity from which spring all great ideas; we should rob ourselves of the precious quality that distinguishes man from all other orders —his determination to think for himself; *to be different.*

This book, then, is based on my conviction that Russia's technological progress forces us forthwith to revise certain attitudes, assumptions, and ways of going about our business. I consider my experience with building nuclear reactors as symptomatic of what is happening in other development projects which will have to be carried through in the future if we wish to maintain our political and economic power as well as a decent standard of living, in the face of the stiff competition given us by Russia and of our own worsening raw-materials position.

Civilization, H. G. Wells remarked, is a race between education and catastrophe. I believe we shall win the race. But not on a 180-day school year; nor if our highest aim is to have a good time and to accumulate lots of material possessions. The poet Matthew Arnold, who spent most of his life trying to improve English education, wrote: "Nations are not truly great solely because the individuals composing them are numerous, free, and active; but they are great when these numbers, this freedom, and this activity are employed in the service of an ideal somewhat higher than that of an ordinary man, taken by himself. Not only the greatness of nations, but their very unity, depends on this."

I began by wanting to remove obstacles hindering my work. My interest was simply to build nuclear reactors. Reactors of all kinds: for submarines, destroyers, cruisers, aircraft carriers, and for central power stations. Anything that interfered with building them as fast as possible was bad. But, as with Plato when he asked "What is Justice?" my investigations led me from the particular to the general and resulted in this present inquiry into the delays which lengthen our lead time so dangerously. Not only in production of things, but in production of well-qualified professional people as well, we now need more time than does Russia or, for that matter, Europe. I believe we must put first things first. This means, above all else, that we must bring excellence to American education. Let us stop fooling ourselves by counting school desks without considering what the children sitting at these desks are being taught. Many of our children are merely parked in the schools. They merely have a good time there. Few get a twentieth-century education.

Our complicated nuclear reactors are but the forerunners of many more projects of even greater complexity, requiring more people with good education and strong motivation. I speak out only because I must. Because in my work I have had a glimpse of the future. The future belongs to the best-educated nation. Let it be ours.

Chapter 2

LEAD TIME AND
MILITARY STRENGTH

Lead time—the time which elapses between conception of a new idea, its development, and finally its fruition in the completed new article rolling from the production lines—is the factor that more than any other is likely to win the next war for the nation which succeeds in reducing it significantly below that of its competitor. Certain assumptions widely held in this country have contributed to a gradual lengthening of lead time from two and a half years during World War II to ten years today. For the good of all of us these must be re-examined. None of us can afford, for our own sake or in the national interest, to wrap ourselves too tightly around our present assumptions and habits.

Assumption number one is that a world war has become so deadly to both sides that men are not likely to start another one.

Assumption number two is that our great edge in productive capacity will prove decisive in the next world war as it was in the first two.

Assumption number three is that our system of capitalist democracy will prevail because it offers mankind the best hope for freedom and for spiritual and material gain.

Assumption number four is that our superior inventive genius will guarantee us a good technological margin over an enemy.

Let us examine these assumptions:

Assumption number one—the deadliness of war.

It is true that there has been a revolutionary change in the nature of war. Conceivably, this change may have ended the danger of war. I pray to God this may be so, but all the evidence of history says otherwise. It certainly is a risky belief and one on which we have not based, and cannot base, our national policy.

Wars have often been started by weak states and by reckless men. Such men, corrupted by power, may fight us again even though they should know that they themselves will be destroyed in the process. We can hope that this will not happen, but we must not allow this hope to influence our judgments or our actions.

Now let us examine the *second assumption—our advantage in productive capacity.*

The production of the free world far exceeds that of Russia and her satellites and allies. Nevertheless, Russia is fast catching up. In 1955, for example, the free world produced more than three times as much steel as the Soviet-dominated world. The United States alone produced almost 40 per cent of the world total compared to Russia's 17 per cent.[1] Other statistics for heavy industry—nonferrous metals, electric power, petroleum, rail transportation, and the rest—are comparable.

Our productive superiority was the decisive factor in both world wars. In 1941–45, for example, we produced as much armament as all the other nations on both sides combined. But several factors are present today which were not present in 1917 and 1941, and which lessen the military effectiveness of our productive superiority.

First, there is the time margin. In both world wars we had the preparation time which comes from not being directly involved in the early fighting. While others fought, we were able to convert to war. Second—and this is really another facet of the same fact—wars moved more slowly then; years were required to wreak sufficient destruction to subdue an enemy. In the interim, a build-up of military strength was

[1] 1956 free world produced 3.8 times as much as Soviet-dominated world.

1957 free world produced 3.7 times as much as Soviet-dominated world.

1956 United States produced 36 per cent of world total.

1957 United States produced 35 per cent of world total.

possible. I think it highly improbable that we shall be as fortunate in a future war, for in the next all-out war the side which moves fastest will most likely destroy the other's capacity to wage war at once. There may be no time to convert industrial plants.

There is also a vast difference today in the manner in which production is utilized in the Soviet Union and in the United States. We use our production to sustain the highest standard of living in history for *all* of our people. The Russians concern themselves very little with the standard of living of the broad masses of their people. In effect, they maintain two standards of living: one, a relatively high one, for a small privileged class; another, very low, for the rest of the population. The first priority of their production goes where their rulers want it to go—to armaments, to capital expansion, to selected development projects, to scientific developments of a spectacular nature, and to the small group chosen by the leaders for a privileged position. The general consumer gets what is left over after these first-priority needs are met. It does not matter much that he lives crowded, many to a single room, that he is poorly clothed, that he must contend with constant shortages of the simplest consumer goods, from buttons to matches. Few Russians have ever known anything better.

We should not fall into the easy error of confusing this low standard of over-all Russian living with their high standard of military production; there is ample evidence of the quality of the latter, and of the high priority given to it by the Russian Government.

The net result of this is that our margin of industrial production is substantially reduced, and in certain circumstances could be completely nullified. There is no longer any guarantee that the side which has the greatest productive capacity has a built-in survival capacity.

The third assumption—that the democracies must win simply because they are right could be the major fallacy of our time. It is very much the same as saying "Virtue will triumph." There have been occasions in the past where virtue has not triumphed. Furthermore, since history is generally written by the victorious side, it is the winner who most frequently stands out as virtuous.

The Russians have a long-range plan which clearly calls for technical, political, and military domination of the world. They have announced that the twentieth century will be the century of communism. And recently Mr. Khrushchev said: "We don't have to fight. Let us have peaceful competition and we will show you where the truth lies. . . . Victory is ours." Having such a plan goes far to counteract the weaknesses and internal contradictions of the Russian system.

We, of course, being a democracy, and dedicated to the belief that government exists for the welfare of its citizens, cannot have such a plan.

The last of our assumptions that we will be protected by our superior inventive genius is, perhaps, the most dangerous one of the four. This assumption is fortified by the comfortable belief many of us have, that whatever anyone else can do, we can do better.[2] Besides which, we do not like to look at facts which are unpleasant. This assumption is also bolstered by statements such as one that appeared in a newspaper on January 1, 1956: "Our greatest asset in 1956 will be the continued prosperity of the United States."

It is important that we spend some time discussing this fourth assumption. A review of Soviet textbooks and scientific papers available in the United States on mathematics and related areas, such as aerodynamics, will show that in some of the most advanced areas of these sciences the Russians do work that is on a par with the best in the West. They excel in the use of large-scale electronic computers, both for solving mathematical problems and for formulating broad attacks on major scientific tasks. American experts who recently examined Soviet calculators stated that these machines matched the most advanced American units of this type. In fact, Mr. Albert C. Hall, research director of the

[2] The speech on which this chapter is based was written and delivered before Sputnik.

Bendix Corporation, said he saw one Russian calculator of a type unknown in the United States.

The Russians are very attentive to fundamental research—to research for its own sake, without any special reference to a particular problem. Witness the considerable number of their young people who are studying astronomy—a number we do not equal.

All this shows up in the excellent job the Russians have done on jet engines, on radar, on long-range weapons, and on atomic weapons. Look how frequently the American public is surprised by Soviet displays of ultra-modern aircraft, naval vessels, and by their work in atomic weapons, and, of course, never more than when Sputnik burst upon us in October 1957. Any competent United States aeronautical engineer who examines published photographs of modern Soviet aircraft can readily deduce that they are doing absolutely first-class work in the aeronautical sciences.

The Russians use the best capitalist incentives to get their top people to do a good job. They also resort to the whip of individual responsibility for their every failure. This concept of nearly complete personal responsibility for a project—somewhat like the responsibility vested in the commanding officer of a naval vessel—can sometimes produce rapid results, as the Russians have shown. But perhaps even more effective are the tremendous material rewards which Russian leaders grant for superior achievement. Thus the leading scientists, educators, top designers, and development engineers in this so-called classless society are "millionaires" compared to the mass of the workers. For example, the pay spread in Russia between an army private and a leading writer, artist, or scientist is more than three hundred to one. In addition to this high pay there are large bonuses. A top aeronautical engineer may receive a number of Stalin prizes and Orders of Lenin; these can raise his pay to one million rubles.

Furthermore, the Russians are expert at exploiting the knowledge of others. Our atomic scientists learned at Geneva in 1955 that the Russians have great respect for American technical literature. They are thoroughly familiar with the technical publications of the Western nations, and they make special efforts to publish the best foreign articles rapidly and to disperse them widely.[3]

Our people also learned that in certain areas important to the Russians, such as electric power and key military technology, they permit considerable latitude to the man in charge. Nor are the top people in research and development penalized quite so promptly or so harshly for failures as are top men in other work. Someone seems to have put across the idea that chances must be taken in these fields, although it is true that a top man will not stay on top very long if he is wrong too many times.

The Russians do penalize severely at the production level. In fact, a considerable percentage of their plant managers are fired every year. They pay a price for this, of course. A plant manager who anticipates a short tenure will not go out of his way and undertake long-range improvement programs. But the Russian system does force to the top a class of managers who are able to achieve production of selected urgent items in low lead times.

There is the achievement of successful earth satellites as one example. But let us look at some lesser-known examples. In 1956 the Russians put into operation a 10-billion-volt proton synchrotron which can accelerate particles up to higher energies than any other machine in the world. We will have nothing to surpass that until 1959 at the earliest.

In late 1955 three engineers from major American corporations toured a large ball-bearing plant in Moscow. One of them, a man from the Automatic Transmission Division of the Ford Motor Company, stated, "I have never seen a better example of automation in my life." The other two agreed.

The second point I would make regarding Soviet industrial capability concerns the rate of progress they are making. Former Senator Benton visited Russia in 1955 and came back

[3] We have since learned more about their excellent translating and abstracting service. This works so rapidly and efficiently that all major foreign technical articles appear in a few weeks on the desk of every Soviet scientist working in the field in question.

to report that their rate of industrial production increases 6 per cent a year. Our own rate of interest at present stands at 3 per cent. This is 50 per cent above the 2 per cent which we experienced for many years. The difference of but 1 per cent has meant a very large increase in national production. Consider, then, what the difference between our 3 per cent and the 6 per cent of the Soviet will mean should it continue.

The Russians have also undertaken a vast educational program to train their people. It began in the early 1930's and is now being accelerated.

I will not elaborate on this subject, for it has been covered thoroughly in many articles and speeches, and the statistics are both voluminous and convincing. They all agree that the Russians are increasing their engineering and scientific talent faster than we are. Mr. Allen Dulles, director of our Central Intelligence Agency, estimated that between 1950 and 1960 Soviet Russia will have graduated 1,200,000 scientists and engineers, compared with 900,000 in the United States. And by 1960 it is estimated she will have more scientists and engineers than we. Thereafter the situation will steadily worsen unless we take steps to upgrade mathematics and science teaching in the high schools and increase enrollment in our engineering colleges. Russia has been catching up with us so fast because each year she now graduates about twice as many engineers as we do.

Other factors make this statistical picture even worse for us. The rate of attrition of Russian engineers and scientists is lower than ours because they are younger and because they do not enter business as do many of ours. We also run into the basic difference in the utilization which is being made of our man-power resources as compared with those in Russia. There the government assigns every engineer to the job where he is most useful to the state. Here there is competition between government and private enterprise for our really first-rate engineers of whom we have too few. The experienced engineer who could be of greatest use in designing complicated military equipment often chooses to engage in design of consumer goods which, though desirable, are not essential to our survival.

The third point I would make is this: Great inventions and revolutionary discoveries in the industrial field are no longer the work of one man working in one laboratory in one country. Inventions today are for the most part the product of men working in groups which are backed by great resources and make use of the ideas of many other men as well. The day of the single creative genius is over. Thomas Edison closed an era. To prove this I ask: How many of you can name the man chiefly responsible for the development of nylon? Of radar? Of the automatic gear shift? Of the electronic computer?

What makes lead time so important today is that the language of invention is now universal. An idea does not come singly to one nation. The same discoveries are being made simultaneously by the scientists of many nations, and they cannot be hoarded to give any state or group of states an advantage. From now on no significant inventions are likely to be available to one country alone for more than a very brief period of time. No great nation can therefore afford to cling to habits of thinking and acting which delay the moment when new ideas are put to practical use.

A discussion I had with an official of a research and development organization exemplifies this. He told me that they had been working for several years on a new metallurgical process which they believed was unknown to anyone else. Recently they learned that three other laboratories had simultaneously been working on the same development; no one of them was familiar with the work the others were doing.

Sooner or later all theoretical knowledge becomes universal. It follows that what counts today is not only inventive genius but even more the practical ability to translate inventions into items rolling off the production line. This is a field in which Americans have always shown particular aptitude. We have it still; witness all the marvelous things which make our life pleasant and easy. But we have not fully applied this aptitude to the cutting of lead time on nationally important items. The Russians, on the other hand, have concentrated all they have in fields which enhance the power of the Russian state. This is why they have been able to improve their military potential so rapidly.

Lead time, of course, has always been a key factor in warfare, from the days when some leader managed to equip his army with stone hatchets faster than his enemy. There has been a tremendous increase in technological complications in modern warfare, and lead time is now measured in years. In 1940, for example, about seventeen thousand man-hours were required to build a military fighter. Fifteen years later the same category of plane required 1,380,000 hours. In 1960, according to estimates, it will be 2,150,000 hours, and that in spite of the fact that man-hour productivity increases continuously.

In a fraction of one man-hour many items can now be produced which a decade ago required several man-hours. To get a true picture of the increased complexity of modern war machines one must therefore factor into the above figures the increased effectiveness of the present-day man-hour.

Here are some typical examples of lead time:

Our armed services have needed three years to design, develop, test, and construct a landing ship for tanks; more than four years for the 57 mm. recoilless rifle, or for a medium tank; five years for a destroyer; seven years for a jet fighter plane; six years for a bomber. It even takes us nearly three years' lead time to effect a change in a uniform. Every United States plane used in World War II was on the drawing boards before December 7, 1941. No plane whose design was started after that date saw action in that war.

Let me illustrate the importance of lead time for military power by citing some examples from modern history which show that the side which was inferior in industrial capacity might yet have won a war had it promptly recognized the potential of a new weapon or reduced the lead time required to bring it into use against the enemy before countermeasures could be taken by him.

Poison Gas in World War I. The Germans used gas shells in a local attack in Poland in January 1915. The experiment failed because of the intense cold. They next used gas three months later in France, in April 1915. But this time the gas had to be discharged from cylinders because the military authorities refused to provide the necessary shells for which the inventor had asked. Even so, a wide breech was made in the French line. However, the German high command had been disappointed with the results of the initial attempt in Poland, and consequently there was neither enough gas on hand nor were troops ready to pour through a four-mile gap where no living defender remained. Two French divisions had completely disappeared. For eight days after the discharge of gas there were large openings in the Allied line, but the Germans were unable to take advantage of this favorable situation.

This was the most complete surprise of the entire war. By failing to have a suitable supply of gas on hand and by not exploiting the opportunity offered, the Germans perhaps missed the one chance to win the war in France in 1915. Once forfeited, the opportunity was lost. In war there is seldom a second chance.

Submarine Warfare in World War I. It is well known how close the German submarines came to winning the war. At one time in 1917 the British forces in France had only four days' supplies left. Had the German authorities grasped the real significance of the submarine, had they begun construction sooner, and authorized its unrestricted use in 1915 instead of 1917, they might well have won the war.

In this use of poison gas or submarines I am not touching on the moral or legal aspects of their use; I am simply discussing their military use.

Tanks in World War I. The idea of the tank was conceived in 1914. It was backed by Winston Churchill, then First Lord of the Admiralty, over official opposition. In September 1915 the British made a surprise attack with tanks against the Germans on the Somme. This premature employment, before large numbers of tanks were ready, was a grave mistake and was contrary to the advice of the tank people. The chance of a great strategic surprise was thus missed. Thereupon the British military authorities lost faith in tanks. Some urged their abandonment, and 1,000 which had already been ordered were canceled by the War Office. But the man in charge of contracting for the tanks was a reserve officer who did not have to be concerned about his future in the Army. He went over the heads of his superiors to Lloyd George, the War Minister, whereupon the order for the tanks was reinstated. In 1918 the German Military Headquarters, in reporting to the German Government that there was no longer any prospect of winning, listed the tank as the primary reason.

Use of the V-2 Long-range Rocket in World War II. The first flying bombs crossed the English Channel in June 1944. They carried one ton of explosive, but because of their straight-line flight and relatively low speed the British were able to cope with them.

Then in September 1944 the Germans fired the V-2, the long-range rocket, but by that time the V-2 could no longer, of itself, win the war. The story could have been different if, starting eighteen months earlier, long-range rockets with increased range, accuracy, and effect had been developed at top priority.

When Hitler finally realized the effect of this delay on the outcome of the war he said to General Walter Dornberger, who headed the German rocket work: "I have had to apologize to only two men in my life. The first is Field Marshal von Brauchitsch. I did not listen to him when he told me again and again how important your research was. The second man is yourself."

These few examples show the importance of rapidly exploiting new ideas. It is not necessarily the most productive nation or the most powerful which will win a war but the one which can develop new ideas fastest—which turns new ideas into hardware quickest.

It should be carefully noted, however, that although the timely use of poison gas, the submarine, the tank, or the V-2 rocket might have caused the loss of Europe to the Germans or of Asia to the Japanese, the United States would still have remained unconquered; not only unconquered but protected by friendly oceans. And with this protection there would have been time for us to develop countermeasures against the new weapons and to bring our industrial strength to bear against the enemy.

The situation today is quite different. There are only two major military powers. If a world war breaks out, these two will be engaged, and there will probably not be time to develop countermeasures against any new and potent weapons. This is the reason why lead time is of such great importance today—why the nation with the lowest lead time has the advantage.

It seems that the Russians have been able to cut their lead time considerably on important items; this is borne out by public displays in the annual air shows over Moscow. Their low lead time, under the conditions of present-day invention and technology, constitutes one of the gravest long-range threats to the security of the Western world. And this is why this problem should be of great concern to all of us.

There are doubtless many reasons for Russian success in this field even though these may be difficult for Americans to understand. One reason is that totalitarian rulers are not answerable to their people. The Soviets constitute a state that for forty years has been organized for permanent and total conflict. In light of this, their accomplishments become more understandable.

I well know the evils and weaknesses of the Russian system, but these are irrelevant to the question at issue. The known weaknesses have not prevented significant achievements and the achievements are no less challenging because they spring from evil motives and may be used for evil purposes. On the contrary, the evils of the Russian system give us all the more reason to fear their technological successes. The greatest mistake a nation can make is to underestimate a potential enemy. Russian engineering and scientific development constitute a threat to our military power. We cannot

allow this challenge to stand and I, for one, do not believe
that a democracy must of necessity be less efficient than a
total state. We can meet this challenge but we may have to
revise some assumptions which have comforted us up to
now, and take action to analyze and improve current methods of producing important military items.

Our scientific discoveries will no longer be of particular
advantage to us if the enemy develops them faster than we
do. Worse still, it has been evident some years now that our
scientific training is deteriorating. Yet we have done little
about it.

The first step we must take is to improve the technical and
scientific training of our young people. We are faced with a
national problem of the first order and nothing less than an
overriding effort by all of us will meet it. There is no lack of
knowledge of *what* must be done. Profound studies have
been made on the subject and much has been said about it.
But so far little has been *done*.

The second step is to take organizational measures which
will speed up design and development of military goods.
This may have to be done by cutting down delays stemming
from too much review, too much coordination, and too many
overhead people—that is, too many purely administrative
men interfering with the creative work of scientists and
engineers. This is not a problem peculiar to the federal government. Private industry is also plagued with it, and knows
that it is. *Fortune* has commented on the subject in an article
called "The Vice-President Problem." *Time* magazine wrote
about it in an article called "Company Conferences—the
Perils of Table-Sitting." A manager of an eastern manufacturing plant estimated that he spends 65 per cent of his
working time in conferences, and that little of this time produces useful results. Important work *can* be streamlined and
the lead time cut down. The money we try to save by checking and counterchecking and by being too careful not to make
mistakes is frequently offset by lengthening lead time. Time,
after all, is money; but time today is more than money; it is
our margin for survival.

We shall undoubtedly discover other ways to improve our technical and scientific development and to cut our lead time once we put our minds to work on the problem. As individuals and as a nation we have to ask ourselves this question: Is the Soviet Union a serious threat to our survival? If the answer to that is "Yes," then we must ask ourselves this second question: Is the nation doing all that it can and all that it should to turn back that threat? If the answer to that is "No," then I submit that something is wrong with us and that we are in trouble.

Let us never forget that there can be no second place in a contest with Russia and that there will be no second chance if we lose. But should we lose, it would be largely by default. It would be because we had acted without vision, because we had wasted the marvelous ingenuity and fine spirit of the American people on production of material things which make life more pleasant at the cost of what makes the republic strong and freedom secure. A high level of material life *may* be bought at too high a cost.

Chapter 3

PIONEERING ON
THE FRONTIERS OF KNOWLEDGE

Capable and ambitious young people could once fashion their lives by their own efforts in wild and unmapped areas of the physical world; today they can still be pioneers—pioneers in the wild and unmapped world of science. Since the birth of modern science, some four centuries ago, enormous advances have been made. But enough remains to be discovered and mapped to guarantee excitement and adventure to more young scientists and engineers than we are likely to have for many years to come.

I recommend that talented young people make their lives an adventure of the mind. This will at times be hard, but always deeply rewarding. Reaping the fruits of one's own intellectual labor, one has a special satisfaction in having been a good cultivator of the talents bestowed by providence. Such pioneering yields not only personal gain and satisfaction, it also contributes significantly to the economic and hence the political strength and security of our country. This is the greatest reward of all.

There never has been a time in the history of our country when it so greatly needed the services of its talented youth. This nation was born on a huge new continent, sparsely populated by less than three million people. I know of no other nation starting life under equally favorable circumstances. Not the least of these was the political inheritance which enabled the founding fathers to devise a form of government marvelously suited to a vast land with fabulous natural resources which had to be developed by a mere handful of people. The Constitution insured fullest scope for each individual's abilities. For almost a century and a half there was always more work than could be done by the available man power. Thus a built-in labor shortage helped us to hold fast to that basic respect of the individual which the first settlers brought with them from England, and which is the foundation of our democratic way of life.

The open frontier kept us socially mobile and therefore checked tendencies toward class barriers which elsewhere so often accompanied advances in civilization; which are indeed characteristic of most highly civilized societies. Respect for the individual, full opportunities for all, abundance of land and natural resources, and a government eminently suited to our particular needs built this nation into the formidable giant it is today.

In recent years, however, some of the foundations upon which we built in the past have begun to crumble or have vanished altogether. Instead of less than three million people, lost in a vast wilderness, we have as of October 1958 175 million, and our annual growth is greater than our total population was on the eve of the Revolution. Virtually no good free land is left except in Alaska. Much of the wilderness that nurtured the free spirit of earlier Americans has disappeared forever. And where even as recently as fifty years ago we exported 15 per cent of our raw materials, we now depend on the rest of the world for 10 per cent of our raw-material needs.

The turning point occurred only a few years ago. Our consumption of raw materials grows at compound rates. If we continued to expand our consumption at this same pace for the next twenty-five years, our needs would reach a fantastic 80 per cent of total world production, leaving only 20 per cent for all other countries. Let me illustrate with a few figures what this momentous change in our raw-materials position, from a resources-exporting to a resources-importing country, portends for our economic health and political strength.

Advances in medicine and public sanitation have quadrupled the world's population since the middle of the eighteenth century, and population is increasing at a geometrical rate. Scientific calculations give us the astonishing estimate that one out of every twenty human beings who have ever trod this earth is alive today. Our own country has the highest percentage of natural increase in population of the large industrial nations of the world, an increase higher even than that of Japan or Italy.[1]

This enormous and ever-growing world population must now be fed and housed on a planet which mankind has exploited unwisely. Soil has eroded over large areas; sea and inland waters have been overfished and in many areas so badly polluted that no marine life can survive. Irreplaceable minerals and fossil fuels have been used up so rapidly that a time can be foreseen when we shall have to do without them. The United States alone, for example, has consumed as much in minerals and fossil fuels since 1914 as had at that time been used by all the world in all of the five thousand years of history since man first discovered bronze. Much of this priceless heritage has been and is being squandered in an appallingly wasteful manner.

Two hundred years ago we were a thinly populated, fabulously resources-rich country. Today we have more than a hundred times more people [2] but far fewer resources. We are, of course, not so poor in resources nor so heavily populated as most of the industrial powers of the world. We are still rich compared to such countries as Britain or Italy. In fact, with but 10 per cent of the population of the free world and 8 per cent of its land area, we manage to consume close to half the free world's volume of raw materials. These figures are frequently used to illustrate that ours is the highest standard of living in the world. What seems more significant to me, however, is that these figures also indicate our increasing dependence on foreign countries for vitally needed minerals and fuels. At present we are truly independent only in two metals: molybdenum and magnesium. When measured

[1] United States annual increase, 1.7 per cent; Japan, 1.05 per cent; Italy, 0.8 per cent; England, 0.4 per cent; and Germany, 0.5 per cent.
[2] 1.2 million in 1750; 150 million in 1950; 1.6 million in 1760; 175 million in 1958.

against our wealth of but a few short years ago, we are therefore poor, and we are poorer still when measured against our future needs.

The shrinking of the once-broad materials base of our industrial civilization makes us, for the first time in our history, dependent on foreign countries for materials which are basic to our technical organization. So far we have had no difficulty buying abroad what we need. We may, indeed, never have to face the disaster which threatens Europe's economic life should the flow of mid-East oil be cut off for political reasons. But it would not be wise to count on this. We shall not remain truly free and powerful unless we compensate, to the fullest possible extent, for lack of materials resources within our own borders. There is one way, and only one way, in which this can be done. It is by using far more effectively than heretofore our natural resources in brain power; we must substitute intellectual resources for diminishing materials resources.

To solve the problem of diminishing materials resources, brain power can devise new ways of extracting at reasonable cost the considerable store of low-grade minerals and fuels still remaining to us which we are not utilizing today because of excessive cost in time and labor. Thus, taconite and shale oil may in time make up for the threatened deficit in high-grade ores and oil. Human ingenuity may discover ways of replacing scarce materials with plentiful materials heretofore unknown or considered unusable, as aluminum is already replacing scarcer copper. Trained minds may be able to relieve shortages of natural minerals and fuels by creating man-made substitutes as plastics and synthetic rubber have become substitutes for much of our imported tin and natural rubber, or as atomic power may eventually replace coal and oil. Similarly, synthetic products made from renewable resources may serve as substitutes for nonrenewable minerals and fossil fuels.

It is a truism that when a society becomes more complex technologically, it needs proportionately more, and qualitatively better, trained professionals. As natural materials resources grow scarcer, the economy depends more and more on its most gifted and highly trained man power. Just as it is far easier to dig a lump of coal from a surface vein than it is to pump oil from a deep well, perhaps buried under tons of sea water, so it is more difficult to release the power locked in the atom than the power held in falling water. Substitution of man-made for natural resources, better utilization of inferior natural resources, elimination of waste—all these demand the raising of our entire body of engineering and scientific knowledge to a higher plateau. I can best illustrate this from my own experience.

A nuclear power plant consists of two distinct parts: the reactor proper, and the heat exchangers, the valves, the pumps, etc., which draw power from the reactor and transform it into electricity. When we began work on the first nuclear propulsion plant we expected that, in building the reactor, radiation hazards would present us with unusual technical problems requiring greater scientific and engineering knowledge than had up to then been needed for construction of conventional power generators. For one thing, the constant bombardment of all metal parts of the reactor by neutrons would in time make the metal itself so radioactive as to change its composition unless we could find metals resistant to such changes. In the end we had to develop two entirely new metals for reactors: zirconium and hafnium. What we had not expected, however, was that we would be faced with almost as many tough problems in the conventional part of the nuclear plant. The problem here again was radiation hazards and resultant difficulty of access to all parts of a nuclear plant for inspection and repair. We spent much time and money testing each item to discover what was needed. Costly methods of trial and error had to be substituted for exact scientific knowledge because the necessary metallurgical knowledge was not available. We did not know *why* conventional heat exchangers, pumps, valves, etc., worked with steam or hydroelectric power plants but *not* with nuclear power plants. Before we can develop a viable and competitive nuclear industry we must raise metallurgy from an art to an exact science, for empirical methods cannot be used indefinitely in modern technology.

In the past man's advances in technology have been slow whenever theoretical knowledge failed to move forward. Rome, for example, had everything she needed to build structures of reinforced concrete except the necessary theoretical knowledge of stresses, thrusts, and distribution of weights. Rome had inherited from Egypt and Greece the practical knowledge in building structures based on lintel and post; from the Etruscans she had inherited the arch; and in Italy she found the raw materials from which she learned by accident to develop a hard and durable cement. Greece had already experimented with strengthening masonry by imbedding iron rods in grooves. Had Rome been able to combine these methods with theoretical knowledge, she could have built her aqueducts and pipelines more durably and far less expensively with reinforced cement.

In a sense we are today at this Roman stage as regards metallurgical science in reactor technology. We must advance our knowledge of theoretical and applied nuclear physics, and we must also raise the entire level of engineering and metallurgy. Similar advances in theoretical knowledge are needed throughout the entire field of science and engineering if technical civilization is to be maintained and advanced in a resources-poor world. How successfully a country manages to raise itself by its own bootstraps to ever higher stages of scientific and engineering competence will determine that country's position in the world. The fate of our country rests in the hands of those of its citizens whose natural endowments enable them to push back the boundaries of knowledge.

I hope that young people who have the ability to grow into empire builders of the intellectual realm will be inspired to venturesome search beyond present boundaries. I hope that they will not let themselves be deflected from pursuing this aim by the lure of better-paying positions having less intrinsic importance; that they will firmly withstand the constant pressure exerted by the advocates of the greatest of modern fallacies that material possessions are the mark of the successful man. Man's acquisitive trait is not what makes him great. Nor can true greatness be measured in dollars and cents. What money value can one assign a book on which the author has labored for years and which may inspire actions having incalculable effects? Is it worth only its price of three or five dollars? How should one value the piece of paper on which Einstein scribbled the simple equation which in its ultimate effects may preserve the freedom of the West by providing it with nuclear power to replace coal and oil? Is pay to be the only measure of the value of a job? No! Nothing material can ever give the intelligent man or woman such deep satisfaction as successful solution of intellectual problems that challenge the mind.

We are engaged in a grim duel. We are beginning to recognize the threat to American technical supremacy which could materialize if Russia succeeds in her ambitious program of achieving world scientific and engineering supremacy by turning out vast numbers of well-trained scientists and engineers. Democracies move slower than totalitarian dictatorships. We have let our educational problem grow much too big for comfort and safety. We are beginning to see now that we must solve it without delay.

I hope that, as they discover the rewards that beckon the modern pioneer in the world of science, more and more talented young people will make the fullest use of their intellectual endowments.

Sometimes we forget that democracy is not a matter of rights alone; that it depends for its very life on acceptance of corollary duties. If democracy meant no more than the right of each citizen to enjoy himself, provided in so doing he harmed no one else, it would be a shabby creed indeed for the people of a great country.

Democracy is not merely a political and social device to insure that under a popularly elected government each citizen may enjoy complete personal freedom, bounded only by the equal rights of other citizens. It is far more than that.

Democracy guarantees everyone freedom and opportunity to develop his mind and character without hindrance from external sources so that he may put them to use not only for himself but for the community as well. It is an inspiring banner under which to fight the enemies of freedom.

Chapter 4

THE MEANING OF A PROFESSION:
ENGINEERING

To practice a profession one must have acquired mastery of an academic discipline as well as a technique for applying this special knowledge to the problems of everyday life. A profession is therefore intellectual in content, practical in application.

The first definition of the term I could find goes back to the time of the Renaissance when Europe's universities became in essence training schools for professional men. The Oxford English Dictionary of 1541 says that a profession is "a vocation in which a professed knowledge of some department of learning or science is used in its application to the affairs of others."

Traditionally, professions have been held in esteem because their esoteric content has been impressive; their usefulness patent to everyone; because of all callings they required the longest and most costly period of preparation; and because they were usually practiced by persons of above-average intelligence, education, and character.

Until well into the nineteenth century only members of university faculties and of the three "learned" professions, that is, theology, law, and medicine, were called professional men. But as human knowledge expanded, new fields of learning developed which could be turned to practical use through new professions or through subdivisions of old professions. Engineering is one of the newer professions.

Engineering had been a skilled craft since remote antiquity and necessarily remained a craft as long as no other sources of power except human and animal muscle, wind, and water were known. It developed from a craft into a profession when it acquired a body of systematic knowledge, that is when scientific advances opened up vast, new sources of energy in nature for the use and convenience of man. Today we have a body of organized knowledge and procedure which requires a lengthy course of professional study. In consequence, engineering now has professional status in most civilized countries.

The term "profession" today has a well-defined and widely accepted meaning. One might, therefore, expect that no vocation would lay claim to this appellation unless it had in fact become an intellectual pursuit monopolizing some department of higher learning. However, we live in a time of growing equalitarianism in all spheres of life. This has brought about a gradual blurring of the distinction between crafts, trades, and professions. Similarly, indiscriminate granting of diplomas and academic degrees has tended to obliterate the traditional distinction between vocational training and higher education. Many people engaged in useful but nonintellectual or routine activities now call themselves professionals.

For example, you can attend a university and study the new academic discipline of "cosmetology," obtaining in due course a bachelor's degree in techniques for beautifying the ladies—God bless them. This is a thoroughly worthy undertaking and I am all for it. But does it become a profession merely because interested parties have endowed a chair in cosmetology?

The traditional hallmark of the professional person, his doctorate, may now be obtained by writing a thesis on a subject such as "Optimum Window Area for a Classroom of Twenty-five Pupils in the Junior High Schools." A doctoral thesis, you remember, is supposed to climax advanced study in an academic discipline by making a contribution through original research in the subject.

Recently I heard of a university that offers courses in television and radio advertising and in gourmet cookery; now it has added to these pseudoacademic subjects a four-year course in trailer manufacturing, dealership, and trailer-park operations. Upon completion of the trailer course, students are awarded a bachelor's degree. They may also take postgraduate work in this fascinating field of higher learning and eventually receive a master's degree, in this way presumably becoming members of a brand-new "learned" profession.

These are examples of what some may consider merely a harmless aberration; one which happens because people like to acquire the symbols of status yet hate to do the hard work which the symbols are supposed to represent. But to my mind it is something more serious. Are we not all extremely indignant, and justly so, when a certain foreign power uses good old words such as "freedom" or "democracy" and twists them around to mean their opposites, thus fooling some people into thinking they are what they are not?

One may even wonder whether institutions that mix salesmanship with science, fly casting with philosophy, and homemaking with history can properly be called "universities"—a term which has a more restrictive meaning, as you will discover if you look it up in Webster's.

Indiscriminate appropriation of words which traditionally have meant excellence of some sort is stated to be democratic. I myself cannot accept this view. Carried to its logical conclusion, each American baby ought then to be supplied at birth with a combination birth certificate, high-school diploma, B.A. and Ph.D. degree! Actually, we are not consistent in this matter. We do not consider it "undemocratic" to respect and reward excellence in athletics, in art, or in business. It would, therefore, seem only just to reserve the honored word "profession" for vocations maintaining the traditional standards of the well-established "learned" professions.

These standards apply both to the content of a profession and to its practice. The intellectual content of a profession, the field of knowledge it monopolizes, must of course be mastered before a man may begin to call himself a professional person. It is not something learned once and for all in a prescribed course of study. Knowledge increases and a man must keep up with it, so he is never done with learning.

In fact, he himself is obligated to carry forward the knowledge on which his profession is based and to insure that it is handed down to new members. In a very intimate sense, his own specialty is a professional man's personal concern and responsibility. The continued advance of a profession can be brought about only by the efforts of its present members who themselves are indebted to the contributions of past members. A professional man who is not able to make original contributions to his field of knowledge can at least work toward enhancing the prestige or standards of his profession. Above all, he can and should support the institutions which train future colleagues.

If professional standards of competence are demanding, so are the standards concerned with professional behavior—with the practicing of a profession. Traditionally, the professional man follows certain tacit or explicit rules of conduct which vary in detail as between different professions. Basic to all of them, however, are two rules: first, the obligation to reject lay direction in the performance of professional work—that is, the duty to maintain professional independence; and second, the obligation to use professional knowledge and techniques solely for the benefit of clients. A clear understanding of these two rules of professional ethics is particularly important for members of the newer professions.

As regards the obligation to maintain professional independence, Flexner—himself an outstanding expert on the nature of professions—remarked: "The essence of . . . professions resides in the application of free, resourceful, unhampered intelligence to the comprehension of problems." [1]

Service ceases to be professional if it has in any way been dictated by the client or employer. The role of the professional man in society is to lend his special knowledge, his well-trained intellect, and his dispassionate habit of visualizing problems in terms of fundamental principles to whatever specific task is entrusted to him. Professional independence is not a special privilege but rather an inner necessity for the

[1] *Universities—American, English, German,* (p. 29), Abraham Flexner (1930).

true professional man, and a safeguard for his employers and the general public. Without it, he negates everything that makes him a professional person and becomes at best a routine technician or hired hand, at worst a hack.

To maintain this freedom, the professional man may have to refuse a lucrative case or relinquish a position with a good salary. In one profession, theology, independence has at times cost the professional his very life. Clergymen of all faiths have shown great courage in resisting the attempts of ruthless governments to dictate to them in matters of religious belief and church administration. These are part of the clergyman's profession—if I may use the term—in which he cannot brook lay control.

Resistance to lay interference is of course easier when a professional man charges fees than when he works for a salary. For this reason, English barristers are professionally prohibited from becoming salaried employees; they must take each case for a separate fee, even when it is tacitly understood that they will accept *all* the cases of a particular client. British solicitors are under no such constraint, but then it is the barristers who are the top men in the legal profession and it is from their ranks that English judges are chosen.

Of the various professions which are indispensable in a civilized modern society, that of members of university faculties ranks high in importance. Professors and researchers are salaried professionals: in most European and in some American universities they are paid by the state. The professional independence of these persons has long been recognized as vital to a nation's intellectual growth. I am speaking, of course, of the principle of academic freedom which is the term applied to the professional freedom of the scholar and the scientist to pursue knowledge wherever it may lead him, even if it leads to conclusions which are politically unpopular. Even so autocratic a country as Prussia understood that without academic freedom her universities would not be able to perform the scientific functions expected of them. Thus we have the strange phenomenon of an express grant of academic freedom in the Prussian constitution of 1850—the only such incidence I have encountered. Sometimes authoritarian governments recognize the inner need of the scholar for this freedom more readily than democracies where egalitarian thinking may consider this to be an unwarranted special privilege.

We have evidence that Russian scholars and scientists are given some academic freedom in strictly limited fields which the government considers politically neutral. Since the Russian people as a whole enjoy no political, economic, or social liberties, even such limited academic freedom apparently suffices to spur the creative abilities of their scientists and engineers. Freedom is a relative thing. The men who push beyond the frontiers of the known are seldom interested in any freedom other than their own driving need. Despite many restrictions, Renaissance scholars, for example, were able to launch a scientific revolution, highly destructive of much that had been implicitly believed for a thousand years and, therefore, bitterly resisted by the authorities. A famous Bolognese philosopher summed up how it was done: "We must speak as the many do, we must think as the few."

Each new profession must fight to gain this freedom for itself. Unless it wins this fight it will not be a real profession. Engineers must be particularly careful not to lose their recently acquired professional status inadvertently. This may happen when they accept managerial positions. In such positions the engineer-manager often becomes a member of an administrative hierarchy where he must submit to lay superiors. His engineering knowledge then becomes incidental, on a par, let us say, with proficiency in a useful foreign language. He functions as an administrator and is no longer a professional engineer.

Even when he takes a straight engineering position in a corporate or governmental organization he has no guarantee that his professional status will be respected. For the engineer often has more difficulty maintaining professional independence than would a physician employed by the same organization. Yet both are experts in their respective fields

—both are professionals. The difference lies in the determination of the medical profession to resist lay interference while the engineering profession does not do this with equal ardor. Toward the physician, the layman is suitably humble in matters medical. Not so, as yet, toward the engineer. This is something for engineers to ponder and to work on, so that eventually their status may become as unquestioned as the doctor's.

Officials in governmental and corporate complexes wield power commensurate with their rank in the organization. They are accustomed to directing the activities of subordinates and they are convinced that their own rank is clear evidence of their superiority over those with less rank. But professional personnel are in a sense outsiders to the organizational hierarchy. Only rarely do their positions accurately reflect their professional abilities. There is, in truth, no such thing as rank among professionals. Each is "master of his fate"; he stands alone, and by his performance demonstrates his own worth. No organization can *give* him his true rating.

Professional persons are a rather troublesome anachronism in organizations although they are indispensable in a technological society. An executive honored by high position and impressive emolument will naturally find it extremely hard to admit, even if only to himself, that in certain matters he knows less than a young engineer to whom he pays but a fraction of what he himself earns. Such dispassionate assessment of one's own limitations is rare and calls for large-mindedness and imagination; for humility in the face of the vast powers with which modern technology deals; for a great deal more understanding of science than is possessed by most laymen.

A frank and perceptive editorial in a recent Dupont publication, entitled "The Great Talent Search," remarks wryly that in competing for qualified professional men, business is handicapped since the *only* incentive it has to offer is money whereas professional and academic life provide *many* intangible incentives. It is but a short step from recognition by business that there *are* other than monetary incentives to the realization that it, too, can provide such incentives.

American businessmen are noted for their ingenuity. They could, I am sure, educate their management people to understand that it is not good business to pay for professional services and then downgrade all one's bright young men to the level of routine technicians. In this connection it is gratifying to observe the growing practice in industry of engaging engineers to direct engineering projects.

Today most engineering is done in association with colleagues on joint projects. Supervision of such groups of engineers by a fellow engineer is professionally indispensable. As long as the man who calls the shots is a colleague, teamwork does not infringe on professional status. This sort of working together is practiced in other professions besides engineering. During surgical operations, for example, one man must be boss and the rest carry out his orders. You can see what I am driving at if you try to visualize a surgical team working under a lay hospital administrator! Eventually I hope that the absurdity of putting an engineering team under a lay administrator will become equally obvious to those who run our huge corporate and government complexes. It's like setting a blind man to lead the seeing.

Creating conditions which will attract engineers and stimulate their productivity is important. But productivity is not the sole consideration; safety is even more important. There is great need for awareness in management of the nature of the forces which science and engineering are now harnessing for the benefit of mankind. These forces are far too complex and too hazardous to be manipulated by technological amateurs.

Long ago a Greek physician sighed: "The life so short, the art so long to learn!" I commend this sentiment to all who supervise complex scientific and engineering projects without themselves possessing professional competence in these matters. It takes a long time and hard study to become a scientist or an engineer. How, then, can even the ablest executive expect to know and understand the details of technical work? Native wit, talent for leadership, even experience in running large organizations—none of these valuable qualities are substitutes for "the art so long to learn."

Perhaps as a people we lack respect for the laws of nature and hence for those who know most about these laws. In popular esteem, the manipulator of men outranks the manipulator of abstract laws and facts, and so we tend to overpay the administrator and underpay the creative professional man. We then compound this error by evaluating the worth of a man's advice by the size of his salary. This lopsided scale of values can stand readjustment. Insistence on professional independence for scientists and engineers may eventually bring this about.

Of course the professional person's legitimate refusal to accept lay control over the manner in which he performs his tasks cannot be twisted into an excuse for incompetence or for blunder. To use the example of an operation again: the surgeon obviously cannot allow the patient's relatives to lean over his shoulder and point out to him where and how he is to make his incision. He must be completely independent of lay direction in the *performance* of the operation. However, the surgeon will most certainly be judged by the *results* of the operation. If too many of his patients die, the public will render judgment on him and he will soon have much spare time on his hands.

This distinction between *dictation of method* and *judgmen of results* is not always clearly understood, particularly in callings which are still in process of developing into professions but have not yet achieved this status. At this stage the prerogatives of professional status may loom larger than they actually are—they may even be visualized as a sort of divine right to escape all public censure for error or failure because of the layman's alleged inability to judge professional work. This would be a pretty nice setup if it could be put across to the public, but I am afraid people won't accept it.

In his dealings with professional men, the ordinary person is of course always at a disadvantage since in professional knowledge he cannot match wits with an expert. He cannot even judge whether a person calling himself a professional is truly an expert in his field. To safeguard the layman against being victimized by quacks and, incidentally, to protect legitimate professionals against competition from unscrupulous impostors, the state usually restricts the right to practice by requiring a license and granting this only upon evidence of proper professional training. Professional associations have gone still further in their efforts to guarantee good service and protect the good name of their members by setting up codes of professional ethics.

This practice varies from country to country, depending on the degree of social importance ascribed by the public to any given profession. Thus in continental Europe the title "engineer" is commonly restricted to persons who have proved their competence to the authorities; in Anglo-Saxon countries it is not so restricted. The professional person's standing in the community depends, in final analysis, on the public's insight into his work, that is, on the educational level of the man in the street. When the specialized knowledge of professional people is incomprehensible to him, the average man is apt to flounder between frustrated suspicion and excessive awe, leading him either to interfere unduly with professional independence or to accept naïvely every claim made by anyone who calls himself a professional. The relation between the expert and the public is one of the central problems of our day.

This problem has been aggravated by a spectacular accumulation of specialized knowledge in the last four centuries. Since rediscovery of classical thought in the Renaissance knowledge has been increasing rapidly. In part, this has been a result of the liberation of man's intellect. This has come about through acceptance of Greek intellectual techniques and eventual expansion of these techniques into our modern scientific methods. In part, it has come about as a result of an enormous expansion of population in the last four hundred years, particularly among people of Western civilization who increased almost twice as fast as the world as a whole. Since the people of the West also outdistance all others in scientific productivity, the sum of human knowledge has grown phenomenally. It now doubles every fifteen years according to available estimates. In contrast, the doubling of population, even in such fast-growing countries as the United States, takes forty years at today's rate of increase. The outpourings of this intellectual horn of plenty are overwhelming. No longer can anyone "take knowledge as his province."

Unfortunately, the average person is touched only obliquely by most of this new knowledge, as when he benefits from some new commodity or service which has grown out of an addition to scientific knowledge. He usually accepts these new things as just another gift from his fairy godmother, Science, and he gives little thought to the manner in which they have been brought about: the long chain of arduous effort which began in a remote laboratory where the germinal idea originated; the long process of applied research to verify its practicability; the detailed engineering to transform it into something useful; and the final step taken by industry and commerce to make it available to the consumer.

While the practical results of increased knowledge merge into our way of life, the knowledge itself seldom becomes part of our general culture. It remains the possession of small groups of experts, each owning that part which pertains to his specialty. This is so not because the experts are selfishly keeping knowledge to themselves, but because most people simply have no taste for knowledge and do not want to spare the time for learning about this potent force in their lives. The gap widens between the experts and the people who depend for their well-being on the work of these experts. This disturbing cleavage exists in the humanities no less than in the sciences. Most people are not well informed in such vital matters as the languages and cultures of the various peoples who share this earth with us; the historic, geographic, and economic background of current events; the place of American civilization in the estimation of the world; and the real strength of our country in the shifting sands of power relations.

The director of the President's Council on Youth Fitness, speaking of the need to improve the physical fitness of our youth, aptly described us as a people addicted to "spectatoritis." We have both physical and mental spectatoritis. We sit in the bleachers and let the game of life unfold before us. We accept the delightful rabbits which science keeps pulling out of its magician's hat without bothering to investigate how it is done. We accept our country's power and strength without worrying too much whether as citizens we are always conducting ourselves as the world expects the people of a great nation to act. We gladly accept all the benefits America has to give us but leave to others the responsibilities that go with them. We measure our own personal worth by the number and quality of material possessions we are able to buy, not by what we make of the God-given capabilities with which we were born.

This passive acceptance of life's benefits and unconcern for the great problems of our day could undermine our freedom subtly and almost imperceptibly. As citizens of a democracy, we are all rulers of this country, and rulers cannot afford to be ignorant of everything beyond the narrow confines of their own small personal world. This was well understood by the upper and middle classes of past societies who knew that their rule depended upon comprehension of the world in which they lived. It was the reason why they made certain that their sons were broadly educated. Intelligence is not the special preserve of any particular class. Learning is hard for everyone. If the middle classes of old were able to push most of their sons through tough schools and universities where they received the liberal education which fits men for leadership, this was not because their sons had superior intellectual capacities but because they were strongly motivated, determined to improve their inherent abilities by training mind and body to their utmost. This motivation came from home and school environments which fostered respect for excellence and emphasized the need of competence in whatever position one occupied in the world. Determination can offset average endowments, but without the desire to improve oneself, the highest native capacities count for little.

Today most Americans have more leisure than the middle and upper classes had in the past. Our country is rich enough to provide the same tough education for all our children which once only middle-class parents required of their sons. But neither our leisure nor the obvious fact that democratic citizens must know a great deal more about their world today than was necessary in a simpler past—neither of these excellent reasons for giving every child a thorough education has greatly influenced popular ideas about education. We have adopted middle-class standards widely in our manners, our homes, our taste in clothes; in all the externals of life. We have not as yet adopted traditional middle-class standards in regard to education. In fact, Americans were more ambitious to better themselves through improving their minds when we were all poorer; when self-improvement meant going to night school after a long day's hard work. The desire for an education which will really stretch our minds is not yet dead but it is almost smothered by our soft and pleasant life. No longer is our national goal a life of adventure, of risk, of a chance to reach for the stars; instead, it has become a desire for comfort and security.

The price to be paid for this comfort and security is too high when it results in ignorance of the powerful forces which control our destiny. Science is now able to change our environment in ways which no one had ever dreamed of. It is disturbing to watch the relentlessly widening gulf separating the minority who understand and make use of science from the uninformed majority who passively accept whatever comes to them from the hands of the experts. That this gulf has not led to conflict or deep alienation—at least not yet—is owing to two phenomena unique to Western civilization: political democracy and professional ethics.

Political democracy vests ultimate power in the average citizen, regardless of his intelligence, education, or sense of responsibility; and professional ethics forbids professional men to take unwarranted advantage of their own superior knowledge. Both of these safeguards we owe to the Greeks. Both were evolved by the Greeks in response to a situation then prevailing where knowledge was concentrated in the collective minds of small groups of experts and spread thinly over the mass of the people. The gap which then existed, say, between the learned men in Egypt who knew how to predict the annual flood of the Nile and the peasant who planted his field in accordance with their predictions—this gap was not much wider than the one between Von Neumann's knowledge of mathematics and that of the average American.

At the dawn of Western civilization the general pattern of life in settled communities was one in which a small group, versed in esoteric knowledge, ruled over the rest of the people to whom access to such knowledge was denied. The legends of many peoples reflect the propaganda of the elite that aspiration to knowledge above one's own station was sinful and would call down the wrath of the gods. Practical knowledge of the kind needed by the peasant, the artisan, the shopkeeper—yes, these the masses might learn. But knowledge of law, medicine, theology, astronomy, the ability to read and write, and to govern, these were a sort of magic possessed only by the divinely ordained few.

Guarded jealously and handed down only within the group, this knowledge provided its possessors with power, wealth, and comfort. In some parts of the world one can even today find people enslaved to experts who use their special knowledge to enforce subordination to their will—shamans, medicine men, and the like.

The Greeks were the first to put the expert in his place. They tore away his mantle of mystery; they denied that knowledge was a special dispensation reserved by the gods for particular groups of people. They threw open the door to knowledge and made its acquisition the supreme civic and human virtue.

They looked upon the universe and man's relation to it as

a proper object of study for *all* men. They believed that everything could be understood by the right kind of intellectual technique. To know, man first had to observe, then to collect and organize his observations; finally to discover what were the underlying, the basic principles in the mass of information on hand. Hard thinking was necessary, but it brought its reward; for once known, these principles could then automatically be applied to new problems. The result might be described as an intellectual chain reaction. It goes far to explain the amazing accomplishments of the ancient Greeks.

Their approach to learning was secular and intellectual; it was rigorous in its insistence on logical deduction from *verifiable* facts. All that was needed to transform this intellectual technique into our modern scientific method was addition of "controlled" experiments and the necessary instruments to do this. Experiments merely widen the sphere of human observation; they permit pin pointing inquiry on specific objects and they bolster deduction through verification by controlled tests. Without laboratories and accurate scientific tools the Greeks were able to create sciences out of conglomerations of unrelated bits of knowledge which had long been possessed by many other peoples. Thus they founded a science of mathematics, of astronomy, of medicine, of history. They gave the West a scientific habit of mind.

Having thought their way out of the then universally prevalent habit of confusing knowledge with divinely sanctioned magic, the Greeks were bound to reject any claim by experts that their special knowledge justified a privileged position. In the political field, this meant rejection of the claim that certain persons had a divine right to be rulers, and so the Greeks were the first civilized people to establish popular rule. Their type of democracy was based on the belief that average Athenians, for example, were quite capable of governing themselves, not only as legislators but even as government officials. Greek democracy required direct participation in government by all adult males. Each was a member of the Assembly and took turns serving his city as soldier, magistrate, judge, and priest. The smallness of the Greek city-state simplified the art of governing, and the absence of a priestly caste in Greek religion permitted lay performance of religious functions.

But this would not have been feasible without a relatively high level of education, and indeed the Greeks were a literate people. Free access to knowledge was the basis of their way of life which differed so radically from that of the people surrounding them—people who were everywhere enslaved by their own ignorance of any except purely practical knowledge. Though a Greek city-state such as Athens did not provide free schooling, the obligation of parents to provide for their sons' education was well understood and accepted. Solon is credited with having hit on a clever device to give sanction to this moral obligation. He released sons from the filial duty to take care of their fathers in old age, if the fathers had not made provision for their sons' education!

Athens in 400 B.C. appears to have had fewer illiterates than many "advanced" nations in A.D. 1800. Moreover, almost anybody could broaden his mind by attending the theater which in Athens had distinctly educational aims besides that of entertainment. "Recreation for the spirit" was available in abundance; one could listen to the philosophers as they wandered about with their pupils, discoursing learnedly and wittily on practically every question or problem known to preindustrial man, and in this pleasant manner one could absorb ideas about truth and beauty which have inspired men ever since. Athens was permeated by a love of learning which most of us would consider excessive. There were eggheads galore and oddly enough the Athenians respected them. They even put up with a man such as Democritus when he uttered the following "weird" sentiment: "I would rather discover one scientific fact than be King of Persia."

Perhaps the most remarkable aspect of Greek democracy was that it did not lead to a cult of mediocrity. On the contrary, education of the young was designed to bring all their faculties to fruition—the suppleness and beauty of their bodies through athletic games, the perceptivity and sharpness of their minds through dialectics, what we would call "public speaking." As Pericles expressed the Athenian ideal, government is in the hands of the people, the law secures equal justice for all, and "as for social standing, our practice is that a citizen who has recognized ability in some field gets public preferment—*it is a question of his abilities, not of his rank.*"

To deprecate the value of classical civilization for modern man is the fashion, but I myself am constantly struck with the lasting validity of so much of what the Greeks and Romans thought and wrote. These thoughts are the basis of many of our most treasured traditions and institutions. Greek political ideas greatly influenced the founding fathers and helped them to devise for us a most marvelous constitutional framework. The Greeks paved the way for modern science, while the Romans still influence the law under which all the people of the West live to this day (even in common-law countries). It is not too fanciful to consider our modern engineering colleges remote descendants of the Greek medical school at Kos or the Roman legal school at Beirut, or even Plato's Academy and Aristotle's Lyceum in Athens.

It is true that Greek and Roman civilizations were based on slavery and that some of their habits and practices were rather odd. Much is made of this by anticlassicist "progressives." And it is also true that outwardly a modern technological society seems to have little in common with Rome and still less with the tiny preindustrial Greek city-state. Yet human problems have a way of persisting unchanged through the most revolutionary permutations of man's environment. The product of clear, logical thought has permanent value. It is, as Thucydides put it, a "possession forever."

Nowhere is this more clearly evident than in the continuing validity of Greek thought about the role of the expert —the professional man—in society. The Greeks evolved the concept that, far from entitling him to a position of power, as everywhere else in the ancient world, the possession of specialized professional knowledge actually imposes on the expert a special obligation, namely to use this knowledge solely for the good of others. This concept is, of course, basic to the position of the professional man in Western civilization. It is foreign to most other civilizations, except where they have deliberately adopted it from the West.

The Greeks founded the first true profession and the science which belongs to it—medicine. They formulated the professional ethics of this profession in the famed Oath of Hippocrates which we have not been able to improve upon. Young doctors embarking on their careers still swear this oath. Its fundamental creed of obligation and responsibility is basic to all subsequent professional codes. All are adaptations of what the Greeks originated.

In this country we have gone far toward cutting ourselves off from the broad stream of Western culture. Rome and Athens are not for our children. Ancient history is supposed to bore them. So they are taught the essence of democracy by joining "smoke-abatement campaigns"; they are shown the utility of simple arithmetic by paying a visit to City Hall to watch the clerks at work. As for learning the languages of the founders of Western civilization, Heaven forbid! Far more useful is it to teach our youth how to drive an automobile and take its motor apart.

I am going to fly in the face of the opinions of all sorts of self-appointed experts on the needs of modern man by suggesting that familiarity with classical thought not only enriches life but is distinctly useful to any professional man. And as a guide to engineering ethics I should like to commend a liberal adaptation of the injunction contained in the Oath of Hippocrates that the professional man do nothing that will harm his client. Since engineering is a profession that affects the material basis of everyone's life, there is almost always an unconsulted third party involved in any contract between the engineer and those who employ him —and that is the country, the people as a whole. These, too, are the engineer's clients, albeit involuntarily. Engineering ethics ought, therefore, to safeguard their interests most carefully. Knowing more than the public about the effects his work will have, the engineer ought to consider himself an "officer of the court" and keep the general interest always in mind.

Since the engineer deals with metals and fuels of which the earth has but a limited supply, it will make a great difference to future generations whether or not he is fully conscious that every ounce of metal or fossil fuel he uses means a diminution of our national patrimony which we bequeath to our descendants.

Engineers build structures which alter man's supply of pure air and water, of food and soil. A poorly designed factory may poison air and water; a dam or highway may needlessly rob our grandchildren of good farm land which by then may well be in short supply. Almost everything the engineer does has an affect on our materials base. His work is seldom purely an engineering task, though he sometimes acts as if it were.

For example, not long ago a bridge was being built across a body of sea water containing valuable oyster beds. A small change of location would have saved the oysters. When this was pointed out by a marine biologist, the engineer in charge of building the bridge rejected the advice out of hand with the contemptuous remark: "What do you know about building bridges?" An irrelevant and rude reply. More to the point would it have been to ask the engineer: "What do you know about building bridges in this particular locality?" In this instance the livelihood of a number of people not in any way involved with the bridge or with hiring the engineer was adversely affected.

To give another example I am familiar with: the design and operation of nuclear power plants. These involve questions of public health and safety which go far beyond those encountered in conventional power plants. For this reason we use every conceivable talent that can help in the design. And when the design is completed, it is gone over in detail

by a committee composed of outstanding specialists in many
technical areas. These men who are full-time professionals
in their respective fields advise the Atomic Energy Commission on the safety of proposed reactor plants. Since reactor safety is a broad problem requiring knowledge of
many subjects, the members of this committee are selected
not only for their knowledge of reactors but for their demonstrated competence in relevant areas such as meteorology,
oceanography, nuclear physics, mechanical, electrical, and
chemical engineering, sanitary engineering; design of pressure vessels, explosives, industrial insurance, and so on.

Consultation with other experts ought to become as common in engineering as it is in medicine. An early Venetian
medical code (about A.D. 1500) made it mandatory for a
physician to consult a colleague before he prognosed any
serious disease. Yet medical mistakes affect only one person,
the patient; engineering mistakes can affect multitudes.

Within the lifetime of all adults a profound change has
taken place in this country which has gone almost unnoticed
by most Americans but which must strike any engineer
forcibly. It is that we have ceased being one of the world's
richest countries in mineral and fuel resources and a great
exporter of raw materials. Indeed, we now depend on imports for many vitally needed materials. As I see it, the most
important aspect of the engineer's code of professional ethics
ought to be the obligation to do nothing that will unneces-
sarily aggravate future resources deficiencies. To my mind
his greatest task is to do everything he can to preserve opportunities for a good life to coming generations who will
not be so rich in land and resources as we are today. This
means, in particular, no needless waste of irreplaceable
materials; no permanent destruction of good soil or of our
shrinking water resources merely for the sake of immediate
advantages; it means utmost ingenuity in substituting abundant materials for scarce materials, renewable resources for
irreplaceable resources. For example, in our nuclear propulsion program we are currently working to eliminate the use
for testing purposes of a scarce gas, helium, by substituting

a more abundant gas. When one is alert to the problem, many ways to save our resources capital will suggest themselves.

Greatly improved education for all and ingenious use of technology will help to offset diminishing land, mineral, and fuel resources. We have only to look at Europe to see what can be done. There a fairly high standard of living is being maintained on a modest resources base.

Switzerland, for example, has only one fifth as much land per capita as we have, yet she manages to produce a per-capita gross national product more than half ours, and only one third less than that of rich and empty Canada. Or, to put it another way, Switzerland has more than twice the population density of India, and she has only rocks, water, and scenery, while India has rich natural resources. Yet the individual Swiss citizen is seventeen times as wealthy as the individual Indian. Improved technology brought about by educational investment in people is the secret of Switzerland's productivity and high standard of living. And technology is the engineer's métier. His is potentially the most important profession because the future well-being of all people may well depend on the manner in which he practices it.

I can think of no better way to raise engineering to the highest professional level than by practicing it in such a manner that every side effect is carefully considered and nothing is done which might conceivably damage fellow citizens, especially those as yet unborn. In fact, I should like to see an engineering oath expressing this sense of responsibility. It might well be something like the ephebic oath sworn by all young Athenians when, at the end of two years of preparation and service, they became full citizens. Each of these young men—called ephebi—promised solemnly to leave his city "not less but better than he found it."

A promise to leave his country not less but better than he found it would be a most appropriate beginning for an engineering career.

Chapter 5

ENERGY RESOURCES AND
OUR FUTURE

We live in what historians may someday call the Fossil Fuel Age. Today coal, oil, and natural gas supply 93 per cent of the world's energy; water power accounts for only 1 per cent; and the labor of men and domestic animals the remaining 6 per cent. This is a startling reversal of corresponding figures for 1850, only a century ago. Then fossil fuels supplied 5 per cent of the world's energy and men and animals 9 per cent. Five sixths of all the coal, oil, and gas consumed since the beginning of the Fossil Fuel Age has been burned up in the last fifty-five years.

These fuels have been known to man for more than three thousand years. In parts of China, coal was used for domestic heating and cooking, and natural gas for lighting, as early as 1000 B.C. The Babylonians burned asphalt a thousand years earlier. These early uses were sporadic and of no economic significance. Fossil fuels did not become a major source of energy until machines running on coal, gas, or oil were invented. Wood, for example, was the most important fuel until 1880 when it was replaced by coal; coal, in turn, has only recently been surpassed by oil in this country.

Once in full swing, fossil fuel consumption has accelerated at phenomenal rates. All the fossil fuels used before 1900 would not last five years at today's rates of consumption.

Nowhere are these rates higher and growing faster than in the United States. Our country, with only 6 per cent of the world's population, uses one third of the world's total energy input; this proportion would be even greater but for the fact that we use energy more efficiently than other countries. Each American has at his disposal, each year, energy equivalent to that obtainable from eight tons of coal. This is six times the world's per-capita energy consumption. Though not quite so spectacular, corresponding figures for other highly industrialized countries also show above-average consumption figures. The United Kingdom, for example, uses more than three times as much energy as the world average.

With high energy consumption goes a high standard of living. Thus the enormous fossil energy which we in this country control feeds machines which make each of us master of an army of mechanical slaves. Man's muscle power is rated at thirty-five watts continuously, or one twentieth horsepower. Machines therefore furnish every American industrial worker with energy equivalent to that of 244 men, while at least two thousand men push his automobile along the road, and his family is supplied with thirty-three faithful household helpers. Each locomotive engineer controls energy equivalent to that of 100,000 men; each jet pilot of 700,000 men. Truly, the humblest American enjoys the services of more slaves than were once owned by the richest nobles, and lives better than most ancient kings. In retrospect, and despite wars, revolutions, and disasters, the hundred years just gone by may well seem like a Golden Age.

Whether this Golden Age will continue depends entirely upon our ability to keep energy supplies in balance with the needs of our growing population. Before I go into this question, let me review briefly the role of energy resources in the rise and fall of civilizations.

Possession of surplus energy is, of course, a requisite for any kind of civilization for it provides the material foundation for civilized living—a comfortable and tasteful home instead of a bare shelter; attractive clothing instead of mere covering to keep warm; appetizing food instead of anything that suffices to appease hunger. It provides the freedom from toil without which there can be no art, music, literature, or learning. There is no need to belabor the point. What lifted man, one of the weaker mammals, above the animal world was that he could devise, with his brain, ways to increase the energy at his disposal, and use the leisure so gained to cultivate his mind and spirit. Where man must rely solely on the energy of his own body, he can sustain only the most meager existence.

Man's first step up the ladder of civilization dates from his discovery of fire and his domestication of animals. With these energy resources he was able to build a pastoral culture. To move on to an agricultural civilization he needed more energy. In the past this was found in the labor of dependent members of large patriarchal families and augmented by slaves obtained through purchase or as war booty. There are some backward communities which to this day depend on this type of energy.

Slave labor was a vital necessity in the city-states and empires of antiquity; they frequently had slave populations as large or larger than their free citizenry. As long as slaves were abundant and no moral censure was attached to their ownership, incentives to search for alternative sources of energy were lacking; this may well have been the single most important reason why engineering advanced very little in ancient times.

A reduction of per-capita energy consumption has always in the past led to a decline in civilization and a reversion to a more primitive way of life. For example, exhaustion of wood fuel is believed to have been the primary reason for the fall of the Mayan civilization on this continent and of the decline of once-flourishing civilizations in Asia. India and China once had large forests as did much of the Middle East. Deforestation not only lessened the energy base but had a further disastrous effect: lacking plant cover, soil washed away, and with soil erosion the nutritional base was reduced as well.

Another cause for declining civilization comes with pressure of population on available land. A point is reached where the land can no longer support both the people and their domestic animals. Horses and mules disappear first, and finally even the versatile water buffalo is displaced by man who is two and a half times as efficient an energy converter as are draft animals. It must always be remembered that while domestic animals and agricultural machines increase productivity *per man,* maximum productivity *per acre* can be achieved only by intensive manual cultivation.

It is a sobering thought that the impoverished people of Asia, who today seldom go to sleep with their hunger completely satisfied, were once far more civilized and lived much better than the people of the West—and not so very long ago, either. In the Middle Ages the eyes of Europe were turned to the riches of the East and these riches induced adventurous sailors to brave the high seas in their small vessels searching for a direct route to the fabulous Orient. The "wealth of the Indies" is a phrase still used, but whatever wealth may be there is certainly not evident in the life of the people today.

Asia failed to keep technological pace with the needs of her growing populations and sank into such poverty that in many places man is again the primary source of energy since other energy converters have become too expensive. This must be obvious to the most casual observer. What this means is quite simply a reversion to a primitive stage of civilization with all that it implies for human dignity and happiness.

Anyone who has watched a sweating Chinese coolie strain at his heavily laden wheelbarrow, creaking along a cobblestone road, or who has flinched as he drove past an endless procession of human beasts of burden moving to market in Java—the slender women bent under mountainous loads heaped on their heads—anyone who has so seen statistics translated into flesh and bone realizes the degradation of man's stature when his muscle power becomes the only energy source he can afford. Civilization must wither when human beings are so degraded.

On the other hand, in societies where a high civilization for the citizenry depended on slave power for energy, abolition of slavery had the immediate effect of reducing energy consumption with consequent decline in civilization. Slavery is incompatible with Christian belief in the worth of the

humblest individual as a child of God. As Christianity
spread through the Roman Empire and masters freed their
slaves—in obedience to the teaching of the Church—the
energy base of Roman civilization crumbled. This, some historians believe, may have been a factor in the decline and
fall of Rome and the temporary reversion of Europe to the
primitive Dark Ages. Slavery gradually disappeared throughout the Western world except in its milder form of serfdom.
That it was revived a thousand years later merely shows
man's ability to stifle his conscience, at least for a while,
when his economic needs are great. Eventually, even the
needs of overseas plantation economies did not suffice to
keep alive a practice so deeply repugnant to Western man's
deepest convictions.

It may well be that it was unwillingness to depend on
slave labor for their energy needs which turned the minds of
medieval Europeans to a search for alternate sources of
energy, thereby sparking the Power Revolution of the Middle Ages which, in turn, paved the way for the Industrial
Revolution of the nineteenth century. When slavery disappeared in the West, engineering advanced. Men began to
harness the power of nature by utilizing water and wind as
energy sources. The sailing ship, in particular, which replaced the slave-driven galley of antiquity, was vastly improved by medieval shipbuilders and became the first
machine enabling man to control large amounts of inanimate
energy.

The next important high-energy converter used by Europeans was gunpowder, an energy source far superior to the
muscular strength of the strongest bowman or lancer. With
ships that could navigate the high seas and arms that could
outfire any hand weapon, Europe was now powerful enough
to pre-empt for herself the vast empty areas of the Western
Hemisphere into which she poured her surplus populations
to build new nations of European stock. With her ships and
arms she also gained political control over populous areas
in Africa and Asia from which she drew the raw materials
needed to speed her industrialization, thus complementing

her naval and military dominance with economic and commercial supremacy.

When a low-energy society comes in contact with a high-energy society, the advantage always lies with the latter. The Europeans not only achieved standards of living vastly higher than those of the rest of the world, but they did this while their population was growing at rates far surpassing those of other peoples. In fact, they doubled their share of total world population in the short span of three centuries. From one sixth in 1650, the people of European stock increased to almost one third of total world population by 1950.

Meanwhile much of the rest of the world did not even keep energy sources in balance with population growth. Per-capita energy consumption actually diminished in large areas. It is this difference in energy consumption which has resulted in an ever widening gap between the one-third minority who live in high-energy countries and the two-thirds majority who live in low-energy areas. These so-called underdeveloped countries are now finding it far more difficult to catch up with the advanced countries of the West than it was for Europe to initiate transition from low-energy to high-energy consumption. For one thing, their present ratio of land to people is much less favorable than was that of Europe and other Western countries when they began to industrialize; for another, the backward countries have no outlet for surplus populations to ease the transition, as did the industrialized Western countries, because the last empty spaces in the world have long since been taken over by people of European stock.

Although most of today's low-energy countries have population densities well below those of some of the most prosperous and advanced European countries,[1] their underdeveloped economies cannot support these lower densities on even a modest level of comfort. These countries must depend on intensive manual agriculture which alone yields

[1] Compare following densities per square kilometer: China, 64; India, 56; Europe as a whole, 84; England, 297; and the Netherlands, 336.

at least bare subsistence for their people. They do not have enough acreage per capita to justify using domestic animals or farm machinery, although better seeds, better soil management, and better hand tools could bring some improvement. A large part of their working population must remain on the land, and this limits the amount of surplus energy that can be produced. Most of these countries must choose between using whatever small energy surplus can be produced to raise their low standard of living or postpone present rewards for the sake of future gain by investing the surplus in new industries. The choice is difficult because there is no guarantee that today's denial may not prove to have been in vain. This is so because of the rapidity with which public-health measures have reduced mortality rates, resulting in population growth as high or even higher than that of the high-energy nations. Theirs is a bitter choice; it accounts for much of their anti-Western feeling and may well portend a prolonged period of world instability.

How closely energy consumption is related to standards of living may be illustrated by the example of India. Despite intelligent and sustained efforts made since independence, India's per-capita income is still only twenty cents daily; her infant mortality is four times ours; and the life expectancy of her people is less than one half that of the industrialized countries of the West. These are ultimate consequences of India's very low-energy consumption: one fourteenth of world average; one eightieth of ours.

Ominous, too, is the fact that despite several unusually good crop years and much effort expended upon improved agricultural techniques, per-capita world food production stands about where it was in 1939. Unfortunately, this apparent balance between food production and population growth hides the fact that per-capita food production has increased only in the already well-fed, high-energy countries but has actually decreased in the undernourished, low-energy countries. Two thirds of the world is probably hungrier today than it was twenty years ago. Despairing, hungry people in these countries are most susceptible to the persuasive siren song of Marxism which promises to perform miracles and produce rapid industrialization—the only way out, so they say, of certain semi-starvation which must come with too rapid population growth in countries already over-populated in terms of their productive capacity. The plight of these people is a human tragedy which wrings the heart. It is also a situation of the greatest peril to the comfortable West. With his usual ruthless logic and brutal forthrightness, Mao has publicly stated that China does not fear an atomic war. She would, he said, be better off if she lost half her present population of 628 million. Mao will soon have atomic weapons, if he does not have them already. With the 300 million men he considers "expendable" as his ace in the hole, he will be hard to trump.

Mao's words are a sort of epitaph marking the last grim consequence of failure to keep energy sources in balance with population. Seven hundred years ago Marco Polo told an awe-stricken Europe of the marvelously prosperous and orderly China of Kublai Khan. China's civilization then stood high above that of the West. She even had an ingenious method of searching out the brightest of her people through an elaborate system of education with graduated examinations. Those who survived these examinations had cultivated minds, though of a peculiarly restricted kind, for this education was the most elaborate machine ever invented for perpetuation of the *status quo:* a gigantic conditioning process which used the best minds of the country to immortalize the wisdom of Confucius and his disciples incorporated in the *Four Books* and *Five Classics,* China's sacred literature. The men who came through the final examination and were thereupon entrusted with high public office could be relied upon to add not one iota to the changeless moral and aesthetic doctrines laid down in the fifth century B.C.; they could be counted upon never to utter an original thought or alter the perfect ordering of the Celestial Empire.

Mental ossification on a high intellectual level prevented China from altering her attitudes and ways of life for millennia. She had, after all, achieved perfection, or so she thought. But the changeless pattern of thought and organization under which China flourished at the time of Marco Polo, when her population was about sixty million, became obsolete as population increased.[2] Though she now has more than ten times that many people, very little was done until recently to increase energy resources. A hard-working, bright, and practical—perhaps too practical—people has now reached the ultimate human degradation when half of China's living human beings are of no use except as atomic cannon fodder which a heartless ruler feels free to sacrifice in the sacred name of Marxism and world conquest.

I think no further elaboration is needed to demonstrate the significance of energy resources for our own future. Our civilization rests upon a technological base which requires quantities of fossil fuels. What assurance then do we have that our energy needs will continue to be supplied by fossil fuels? The answer is, in the long run, none.

The earth is finite. Fossil fuels are not renewable. In this respect our energy base differs from that of all earlier civilizations. They *could* have maintained their energy supply by careful cultivation. We cannot. Fuel that has been burned is gone forever. Fuel is even more evanescent than metals. Metals, too, are nonrenewable resources threatened with eventual extinction, but something can be salvaged from scrap. Fuel leaves no scrap and there is nothing man can do to rebuild exhausted fossil fuel reserves. They were created by solar energy five hundred million years ago and took eons to grow to their present volume.

In the face of the basic fact that fossil fuel reserves are finite, the exact length of time these reserves will last is important in only one respect: the longer they last, the more time we have to invent ways of living off renewable or substitute energy sources and to adjust our economy to the vast changes which we can expect from such a shift.

Fossil fuels resemble capital in the bank. A prudent and responsible parent will use his capital sparingly in order to

[2] China grows at the rate of 2 per cent per year; India, 1.7 per cent, United States, 1.7 per cent; world as a whole, 1.7 per cent.

pass on to his children as much as possible of their inheritance. A selfish and irresponsible parent will squander it in riotous living and care not one whit how his offspring will fare.

Engineers whose work familiarizes them with energy statistics, farseeing industrialists who know that energy is the principal factor which must enter into all planning for the future, responsible governments who realize that the wellbeing of their citizens and the political power of their countries depend on adequate energy supplies—all these have begun to be concerned about energy resources. In this country, especially, many studies have been made in the last few years seeking to discover accurate information on fossil fuel reserves and foreseeable fuel needs.

Statistics involving the human factor are, of course, never exact. The size of usable reserves depends on the ability of engineers to improve the efficiency of fuel extraction and use. It also depends on discovery of new methods to obtain energy from inferior resources at costs which can be borne without unduly depressing the standard of living. Estimates of future needs, in turn, rely heavily on population figures which must always allow for a large element of uncertainty, particularly as man reaches a point where he is more and more able to control his own way of life.

Current estimates of how long fossil fuel reserves will last vary to an astonishing degree. In part this is because the results differ greatly if cost of extraction is disregarded or if population growth is not taken into consideration, or, what is equally important, not enough weight is given to increased fuel consumption required to process inferior or substitute metals. We are rapidly approaching the time when exhaustion of better-grade metals will force us to turn to poor grades requiring in most cases greater expenditure of energy per unit of metal.

But the most significant distinction between optimistic and pessimistic fuel-reserve statistics is that the optimists generally speak of the immediate future, the next twenty-five years or so, while the pessimists think in terms of a century from now. A century, or even two, is a short span in the history of a great people. It seems sensible to me to take a long view even if this involves facing unpleasant facts.

It is an unpleasant fact that according to our best estimates total fossil fuel reserves, recoverable at not more than twice today's unit cost, are likely to run out at some time between the years 2000 and 2050 if present standards of living and population growth rates are taken into account. Oil and natural gas will disappear first; coal last. There will be coal left in the earth, of course, but it will be so difficult to mine that energy costs would rise to economically intolerable heights, so that it would then become necessary either to discover new energy sources or drastically to lower standards of living.

For more than one hundred years we have stoked ever-growing numbers of machines with coal; for fifty years we have pumped gas and oil into our factories, cars, trucks, tractors, ships, planes, and homes without giving a thought to the future. Occasionally the voice of a Cassandra has been raised only to be quickly silenced when a lucky discovery revised estimates of our oil reserves upward, or a new coal field was found in some remote spot. Fewer such lucky discoveries can be expected in the future, especially in industrialized countries where extensive mapping of resources has been done. Yet the popularizers of scientific news would have us believe that there is no cause for anxiety, that reserves will last thousands of years, and that before they run out science will have produced miracles. Our past history and security have given us the sentimental belief that the things we fear will never really happen—that everything turns out right in the end. But prudent men will reject these tranquilizers and prefer to face the facts so that they can plan intelligently for the needs of their posterity.

Looking into the future from the mid-twentieth century we cannot feel overly confident that present high standards of living will of a certainty continue through the next century and beyond. Fossil fuel costs will soon definitely begin to rise as the best and most accessible reserves are exhausted, and more effort will be required to obtain the same energy from remaining reserves. It is likely also that liquid fuel synthesized from coal will be more expensive. Can we feel certain that when economically recoverable fossil fuels are gone science will have learned how to maintain a high standard of living on *renewable* energy sources?

I believe it would be wise to assume that the principal renewable fuel sources which we can expect to tap before fossil reserves run out will supply only 7 to 15 per cent of future energy needs. The five most important of these renewable sources are wood fuel, farm wastes, wind, water power, and solar heat.

Wood-fuel and farm wastes are dubious as substitutes because of growing food requirements to be anticipated. Land is more likely to be used for food production than for tree crops; farm wastes may be more urgently needed to fertilize the soil than to fuel machines.

Wind and water power can furnish only a very small percentage of our energy needs. Moreover, as with solar energy, expensive structures would be required, making use of land and metals which will also be in short supply. Nor would anything we know today justify putting too much reliance on solar energy though it will probably prove feasible for home heating in favorable localities and for cooking in hot countries, such as India, that lack wood.

The outlook for nuclear fuels is more promising. These are not, properly speaking, renewable energy sources, at least not in the present state of technology, but their capacity to "breed" and the very high-energy output from small quantities of fissionable material, as well as the fact that such materials are relatively abundant, do seem to put nuclear fuels into a separate category from exhaustible fossil fuels. The disposal of radioactive wastes from nuclear power plants is, however, a problem which must be solved before there can be any widespread use of nuclear power.

Another limitation on the use of nuclear power is that we do not today know how to employ it other than in large units to produce electricity or to supply heating. Because of its inherent characteristics, nuclear fuel cannot be used directly in small machines, such as cars, trucks, or tractors. It is doubtful whether it could in the foreseeable future furnish economical fuel for civilian airplanes or ships, except very large ones. Rather than trying to build nuclear locomotives, we may find it more advantageous to move trains by electricity produced in nuclear central stations. We are only at the beginning of nuclear technology, so it is difficult to predict what we may expect.

Transportation—the lifeblood of all technically advanced civilizations—seems to be assured once we have borne the initial high cost of electrifying railroads and replacing busses with streetcars or interurban electric trains. But unless science can perform the miracle of synthesizing automobile fuel from some energy source as yet unknown or unless trolley wires power electric automobiles on all streets and highways, it will be wise to face up to the possibility of the ultimate disappearance of automobiles, trucks, busses, and tractors. Before all the oil is gone and hydrogenation of coal for synthetic liquid fuel has come to an end, the cost of automotive fuel may have risen to a point where private cars will be too expensive to run and public transportation will again become a profitable business.

Today the automobile is the most uneconomical user of energy. Its efficiency is 5 per cent compared with 23 per cent for the diesel-electric railway. It is the most ravenous devourer of fossil fuels, accounting for more than half of the total oil consumption in this country. The oil we use in the United States in one year took nature about fourteen million years to create. Curiously, the automobile, which is the greatest single cause of the rapid exhaustion of oil reserves, may eventually be the first fuel consumer to suffer. Reduction in automotive use would necessitate an extraordinarily costly reorganization of the pattern of living in industrialized nations, particularly in the United States. It would seem prudent to bear this in mind in future planning of cities and industrial locations.

Our present known reserves of fissionable materials are

many times as large as our net economically recoverable reserves of coal. A point will be reached before this century is over when fossil fuel costs will have risen high enough to make nuclear fuels economically competitive. Before that time comes we shall have to make great efforts to raise our entire body of engineering and scientific knowledge to a higher plateau. We must also induce many more young Americans to become metallurgical and nuclear engineers or else we shall not have the knowledge or the trained people to build and run the nuclear power plants which ultimately may have to furnish the major part of our energy needs. If we start to plan now, we may be able to achieve the requisite level of scientific and engineering knowledge before our fossil fuel reserves give out, but the margin of safety is not large. All this is based on the assumption that atomic war can be avoided and that population growth will not exceed that now calculated by demographic experts.

War, of course, cancels all man's expectations. Even growing world tension just short of war could have far-reaching effects. In this country it might, on the one hand, lead to greater conservation of domestic fuels, to increased oil imports, and to acceleration in scientific research which might turn up unexpected new energy sources. On the other hand, the resulting armaments race would deplete metal reserves more rapidly, hastening the day when inferior metals must be utilized with consequent greater expenditure of energy. Underdeveloped nations with fossil fuel deposits might be coerced into withholding them from the free world or may themselves decide to retain them for their own future use. The effect on Europe, which depends on coal and oil imports, would be disastrous and we would have to share our own supplies or lose our allies.

Barring atomic war or unexpected changes in the population curve, we can count on an increase in world population from 2½ billion in 1950 to between 4 and 5 billion in the year 2000; 6 to 8 billion by 2050. The United States grows at the same annual rate as the world as a whole—1.7 per cent. In fact, the world did not catch up with us until 1957. Surprising as it may sound, we may expect to have a population equal to that of India today (392 million) in just fifty years, and of present-day China (628 million) in but eighty years.

It is an awesome thing to contemplate a graph of world population growth from prehistoric times—tens of thousands of years ago—to the day after tomorrow—let us say the year A.D. 2000. If we visualize the population curve as a road that starts at sea level and rises in proportion as world population increases and if, furthermore, we let one mile represent one year in the history of mankind, we should get this picture: the road would stretch endlessly almost level for 99 per cent of the time that man has inhabited the earth. Then in 6000 B.C., when history may be said to have begun, we see the road running at roof-top level of a six-story apartment house (seventy feet). From here it ascends almost imperceptibly for 7,000 miles to a level that would correspond to twice the height of a skyscraper (1,600 feet). The graduation now becomes steeper and in the next 400 miles the road reaches a height (2,900 feet) corresponding to three times that of the Eiffel Tower. In the last 400 miles of this very long journey the road suddenly turns sharply upward at an almost perpendicular inclination and goes straight up to an elevation of 29,000 feet—the height of Mount Everest, the world's tallest mountain.

In the 8,000 years from the beginning of recorded history to the year A.D. 2000 world population will thus have grown from 10 million to 4 billion,[3] with 90 per cent of the growth taking place during the last 5 per cent of that period, that is, in four hundred years. It took three thousand years to accomplish the first doubling of population, one hundred years

[3] Based on the most careful and conservative estimates of demographers I could find two years ago. Recent U.N. statistics indicate that these estimates may have been too conservative and we may well reach the 4-billion mark for the world as a whole in but twenty years, or about 1980. Incidentally, at our present growth rates, the United States alone will reach a 4-billion population about 2150, thus telescoping the growth rate of the world as a whole in the short space of five hundred years—from 1650 to 2150!

for the last doubling, but the next doubling will require only forty years.

The rapidity of population growth has not given us enough time to readjust our thinking. A century and a half ago our country was a wilderness in which a pioneer could find complete freedom from men and from government. If things became too crowded—if he saw his neighbor's chimney smoke—he could, and often did, pack up and move West. For much of our history we were a vast country with too few people to bring it under cultivation. We conserved what was scarce—human labor—and squandered what seemed abundant—natural resources—and we are still doing the same today.

Much of the wilderness that nurtured what is most dynamic in the American character is now buried under cities, factories, and suburban developments where each picture window looks out on nothing more inspiring than the neighbor's back yard with the smoke of his fire in the wire basket clearly visible. Life in crowded communities cannot be the same as life on the frontier. We are no longer free, as was the pioneer, to work for our own immediate needs regardless of the future. We are no longer as independent of men and of government as were Americans two or three generations ago. An ever larger share of what we earn must go to pay for services caused by crowded living—bigger governments; bigger city, state, and federal budgets to pay for more public services. Merely to supply us with enough water and to carry away our waste products gets daily more difficult and expensive. More laws and law-enforcement agencies are needed now to regulate human relations in urban industrial communities and on crowded highways than in the America of Thomas Jefferson.

Certainly no one likes taxes, but we must become reconciled to larger taxes in the larger America of tomorrow.

I suggest that this is a good time to think soberly about our responsibilities to our descendants—those who will ring out the Fossil Fuel Age. Our greatest responsibility, as parents and as citizens, is to give America's youngsters the best possible education. We need the best teachers and enough of them to prepare our young people for a future immeasurably more complex than the present, and calling for ever larger numbers of competent and highly trained men and women. This means that we must not delay building more schools, colleges, and playgrounds. It means that we must reconcile ourselves to continuing higher taxes to build up and maintain at decent salaries a greatly enlarged corps of much better trained teachers, even at the cost of denying ourselves such momentary pleasures as buying a bigger new car, or a TV set, or a household gadget. We should find, I believe, that these small self-denials would be more than offset by the benefits they would buy for tomorrow's America. We might even, if we wanted to, give a break to these youngsters by cutting fuel and metal consumption a little here and there so as to provide a safer margin for the necessary adjustments which eventually must be made in a world without fossil fuels.

There is also another thing to consider: high-energy consumption has always been a prerequisite of political power. The tendency is for political power to be concentrated in an ever smaller number of countries. Ultimately, the nation that controls the largest energy resources will become dominant. If we give thought to the problem of energy resources, if we act wisely and in time to conserve what we have and prepare well for necessary future changes, we shall insure this dominant position for our own country.

Chapter 6

INVESTMENT IN
HUMAN RESOURCES

Whatever the world of tomorrow may turn out to be, one thing is certain. Greater mental effort will be required of all mankind. This is but a consequence of advance in civilization. In primitive societies men survived if they had native wit, physical courage, and strength, and also a modicum of good luck. Not much more was required of their leaders. As life daily becomes more complex—more artificial, fashioned less by natural forces than by human action—these simple human qualities no longer suffice. Others must come to the fore. None will be more important than possession of a mind well stocked with basic facts and able to think clearly, unemotionally, and independently.

Even today these qualities are needed by every citizen of a democracy, for each shares in making final decisions on national problems of great complexity and many-faceted import. In the future it will be more difficult to reach the right decisions. Problems will rarely turn on simple questions of right or wrong which any honest man of normal intelligence can readily grasp. To decide complicated matters we must be able to judge policies against over-all national needs and the realities of our political and economic position in the world. We cannot make logical decisions unless we have familiarized ourselves with the pertinent facts. This may require a habit of always consulting reliable sources of information rather than accepting glib public statements, and the ability to think through a thicket of special pleading and go to the heart of the matter. None of us is born with this kind of mental discipline. We learn it through effort, application, and many years of formal schooling. Today all advanced coun-

99

tries know that without schools they cannot continue to maintain their complex modern way of life. This is because life in a modern industrial state demands a great deal more "book learning" of everyone who wants to make a good living for himself and his family. These advanced countries, therefore, provide for the formal education of *all* their children.

In totalitarian countries a *subject* is properly educated when he has learned enough to do his work efficiently, whether as a typist, doctor, or top scientist. In democratic countries a *citizen* must learn all this and much more besides. He must prepare himself not merely for competence in his chosen calling but must also learn to become a responsible citizen and a contented human being. He needs to learn how to lead a good life no less than an efficient one. Above all, he must be taught how to use his mind independently so that he may be a free man.

A much higher quality of education is required to turn children into thinking men than to turn them into merely competent men. Democratic education must do both. Never before have we been in greater need of people capable of good hard thinking than we are today. Man rose from savagery by putting his mind to work. He has now so remade the world that only the most intensive use of his brain power can insure his survival in decency.

Almost two centuries ago Jefferson warned solemnly that for a nation to expect to be both "ignorant and free, in a state of civilization," would be to expect "what never was and never will be." The operative words here are "in a state of civilization." Ignorance can be tolerated in primitive communities; it is disastrous in civilized societies.

The rate of progress or decline of a country is so closely tied to the education it gives its children that one might call this rate a function of education. A wise country knows that its best investment for the future is effort and money put into schools. Every country educates its children, whether informally by the father's advice and example, as in primitive agricultural and handicraft societies, or formally in schools, as in modern countries. At different stages of history different kinds of education are needed. Life does not stand still; neither can a nation. It either advances or it retreats, and it will retreat if it tries to stand still. For these reasons education must continually be kept under close scrutiny to insure that it will always produce the kind of people needed at any given moment in time.

Everyone is aware today that our educational system has been allowed to deteriorate. It has been going downhill for some years without anything really constructive having been done to arrest the decline, still less to reverse its course. We thus have a chronic crisis; an unsolved problem as grave as any that faces our country today. Unless this problem is dealt with promptly and effectively the machinery that sustains our level of material prosperity and political power will begin to slow down. This may take a little time and we, who neglect our civic responsibility by postponing action, may be lucky enough to escape the consequences. The ones who assuredly will have to pay are now growing up fast or are as yet unborn. In truth, the sins of the fathers are visited on their children.

The crisis is one of inadequate funds for education and of inadequate content of education. The first is easier to deal with. Here are the financial problems we face:

In 1870 about 57 per cent of the five- to 17-year-olds were enrolled in elementary and high school and this percentage rose steadily every year until it reached approximately 85 per cent in 1940. Since then the percentage has decreased slightly. For eighty years total public elementary and high-school enrollment increased by about 2½ to 3½ million every decade. Taxes kept up fairly well with this expansion, but beginning in 1950 the whole situation changed with astonishing rapidity. Enrollments suddenly increased at five times the rate that had prevailed for so many decades. Fourteen million pupils have entered our schools in the last eight years, boosting our total school population from 25 million to 39 million, or 57 per cent. In budgeting school expenses we must consider this rate of increase, that is about 17.5

million new pupils every decade, as a *minimum* normal
growth rate. It may well rise considerably as total United
States population increases.

In the face of this unprecedented reversal of a long-time
trend, taxes were not raised fast enough or high enough.
Figured in stable dollars, 1958 expenditures on public education have indeed risen over 1950 expenditures by approximately 78 per cent. This admittedly large increase is still not
sufficient for we must provide not only for increased costs of
running the schools but also for a continuous building program. Our educational plant should have expanded 57 per
cent in the last eight years merely to house the new pupils,
and to this must be added necessary replacement of over-age
buildings. Classroom space for a student cost about one thousand dollars. To maintain the *status quo* would thus have
cost 14 billion dollars. Our crowded schools—some operating
on double shifts—are eloquent testimony that we have not
kept school capital investment in line with growth of school
population. The situation will presently become worse as
the postwar babies graduate from high school and clamor for
admittance to the colleges. Then even more money will be
needed to provide each student with classroom and dormi-
tory space.

No plant manager would be so foolish as to increase his
working force without making the necessary capital investment to give new workers the space and tools they need. Yet
as a nation we act with less foresight. For example, *Fortune*
magazine reports that in 1957 we spent 50 billion dollars for
capital investment in industrial, transport, utilities, commercial, and farm enterprises. Would it be too great a sacrifice
to invest, let us say, 1½ billion dollars each year in construction of new schools? To give perspective, consider that according to the American Automobile Association, Americans
invest 14 billion dollars, or 4.7 per cent, of disposable income
on personal transportation—the family car. This is almost
ten times what would have to be invested in new schools if
we merely tried to maintain the *status quo*. We spend 5.3
per cent of disposable income for maintenance of our cars,

and this is one and a half times what we spend for maintenance of our public elementary and high schools. There are some elegant suburbs in this country where almost every boy has a car of some sort by the time he is old enough to get a license but where he goes to school on a two-shift basis! Can we afford to go on putting more of our money into acquisition of tangible property for ourselves than in buying the intangible asset of a good education for our children—a possession worth more than even the shiniest Cadillac?

Just as every worker must be backed by considerable capital investment in plant and machinery—some ten thousand dollars per man, I believe—so must each pupil be backed by the necessary capital investment in educational plant and facilities. In the period 1940–54, during which we upped educational expenditures 78 per cent, we benefited from an increase in the gross national product of 192 per cent (in constant 1947 dollars). We preferred to spend the lion's share of this windfall on ourselves rather than on the education of our children.

Consequently, there has set in a slow attrition, a corroding of the intellectual supports which maintain our high level of technology and hence our pleasant standard of living. This has happened largely, I believe, because we did not adjust our thinking fast enough to a situation unprecedented in our history. In this country we habitually think in terms of scarcity of people rather than abundance. Since this has been true during almost all our history, it is not surprising that we still think in terms of this but recently vanished past.

America represented a fabulous opportunity to those who came to her shores—a sleeping beauty of a land surrounded by oceans as difficult to cross in sailing ships as it is for a man on foot to penetrate a thicket of thorns.

We have no other recorded instance of a civilized people obtaining possession of a vast new empty land with all these favorable characteristics: excellent climate, great natural resources, and an advantageous geographic location. With their superior techniques, the newcomers could rapidly exploit its great natural wealth and thus, merely for the taking, achieve a material level of life impossible in old and populous lands. Even the primitive ancestors of the American Indian, wandering across the Bering Strait, must have found this a land of plenty. Theirs, too, was a good life until the white man came—a life incomparably better than anything they had experienced in their Asian homelands. Without European techniques the Indians could not, of course, make use of the minerals and fuels buried in our earth. They benefited from the abundance of our land which gave them elbowroom, and thus a sense of personal freedom, no less than from its fertile soil from which food was easy to obtain. They could not defend their rich land against the Europeans because they lacked technical competence. It passed from them to us, its beauty unspoiled, its wealth intact.

For all who came here America stood for limitless space and wealth. Yet even the largest country will fill up rapidly if its population grows fast enough; even the richest in natural resources will in time become poor if these are ruthlessly mined and foolishly used. Nothing earthly is limitless. To grasp this fact fully is not easy. It takes time to change deep-seated ways of thinking which have long accorded with reality.

It has taken us too long to recognize the significance of a fact we hear endlessly on the radio: that 11,000 babies are born every day in this country. We have therefore failed to prepare for the educational needs of these babies which will begin six years after birth. They will need a million *extra* desks in elementary school each and every year henceforth. As they go through school, at current drop-out rates, 875,000 *extra* desks in high school and more than a quarter of a million *new* places in college must be made ready for them. This annual increase must be factored into all our estimates of expenditures for education. This we have not done.

We have a continuing crisis in education caused by poor planning although our requirements could so easily have been foreseen. In today's rapidly changing world this is a fatal error. Nations decline if they are not continually alert to the needs of the future. The law of life is "adapt or perish."

What we do today was largely determined for us by the vision and by the actions of those who preceded us. So will tomorrow's events in large measure depend on what we plan and do today.

We must spend substantially more for education. We must also spend school tax money more wisely. I venture to say that of all leading countries, we get the least in education for our tax dollars. For various reasons our school establishment is the most expensive in the world. We have set ourselves standards of luxury in buildings and equipment unknown elsewhere. We require two to three years longer to bring our students to approximately the same level of education as those in most European countries—this alone means 20 per cent higher costs for the same end product. Although we spend a slightly greater percentage of our national income on public education than the leading countries of Europe, but less than Russia, these costs are more easily borne by us since we are the richest nation in the world. We may feel that we are taxing ourselves highly for our children, but we spend almost as much for alcoholic beverages as for elementary and secondary schools combined. We put nearly as many dollars into advertising in order to sell goods for which there is no pressing need—else why advertise?—than into the production of well-educated high-school graduates which we need urgently. This means that our national outlay for the education of *citizens* is approximately the same as our outlay for the education of *consumers*. We spend more money for comic books than for all textbooks used in elementary and high schools.

What these figures show is that it would be no great hardship to invest money in our children's future, but they are not a guide which will help us find a way to raise the necessary funds. We have here a national problem which is difficult to solve and upon which we the people must act to the best of our ability. In the light of the imperative need for educated citizens should we not perhaps re-examine our fear of federal aid to education? Although many of our poorer regions tax themselves proportionately more heavily than wealthier sections of the country, their schools still remain inferior, which makes it a gamble as to whether a child receives a fair education or a poor one. Many other countries have traditions of local control and financing of schools but have still found ways to bring the help of their national government to bear without setting up a national dictatorship over education. England and Switzerland, for example, have worked out excellent partnerships between central government and local community. We might learn from them. It is foolish to let national pride stand in the way.

Comparing notes with other countries, we should find that they put most of their money into teachers and make do with simple, almost austere school buildings. Basically, school is nothing but a teacher surrounded by a group of children. If the teacher is excellent, the children will learn much and in doing so be happy as well. As long as the room is light and large enough, warm in winter, and supplied with the minimum of necessary teaching tools, it will suffice. If these fundamentals are paid for and there is a surplus, additional facilities can quickly be added. It takes only two years to build a school against four to five years to train a public schoolteacher and additional years for her to acquire the experience which makes for inspired teaching. A college professor must add to this several more years to complete his preparation for teaching.

It is obvious, therefore, that we must plan in advance for a period of eight to ten years. We must take into consideration that at the beginning of each school year all our educational institutions will find their enrollments well above those of the preceding year and make preparations for having the requisite number of additional teachers ready on time. Instead, as everyone knows, teachers are leaving the schools in large numbers because their salaries have not kept up with those in other professions; have, in fact, fallen below those of production workers in manufacturing industries. The steep drop in purchasing power has adversely affected the desirability of the academic career as compared to other professions. The results are particularly disastrous at the highest level of teaching in college and university for, let us never forget, college professors are capable people who can turn their hands to a variety of vastly more remunerative jobs if driven too far. We have come to a point where we pay them so little that they can no longer even purchase their own product: with college tuitions having risen greatly, few professors can afford to send all their children through college.

In any profession, and particularly in the teaching profession, there are dedicated people who will work under adverse conditions and at low pay. But we must not delude ourselves that the answer to our dilemma lies solely in dedicated people. There will never be enough of them. We are not entitled to educate our children on the philanthropy of our teachers. Whether we like it or not, in the culture which exists in the United States today the desirability of a given occupation is measured largely in terms of salary. This explains why the ablest young men and women are turning away from teaching even though numerous scholarships and fellowships are available. No such recruitment problem exists, for example, in the well-paid professions such as medicine or law. These have no lack of applicants; in fact, many are turned away.

When the income of teachers rises to the point where it competes with other professions, it will draw the right kind of people.

Therefore, I submit that an immediate step in solving our educational problem is to increase salaries drastically. It little matters that some teachers will be overpaid. The low salaries paid for the last fifty years have been responsible for the presence in the teaching profession of many who are not really qualified. It will profit us very little to spend millions of dollars on scholarships and then place the students under incompetent teachers. In the long run, increasing teachers' salaries is the surest way to obtain more competent men and women. Further, when salaries are increased it will be possible to base advancement on performance and not on seniority.

Unless we quickly remedy the present treatment of our teaching and scholarly resources we shall inevitably have morally and intellectually incompetent teaching staffs. Eventually the bright young man will sacrifice his desire to teach in order to provide adequate standards of comfort, decency, and security for his family. The movement away from teaching will continue at an increasingly rapid rate.

We all know of the nationwide shortage of elementary and high-school teachers. What is not evident is the real meaning of this shortage. Few classrooms are ever closed because a teacher is lost. What happens is that teaching standards are lowered or the class size is raised. Both of these accommodations have already taken place and may well become the general rule. When a teacher with the desired qualifications is not available, someone less qualified is hired. The teacher then becomes, in effect, a "baby sitter."

The result of this niggardly payment of our teachers—of those upon whom we depend to transmit our culture and our civilization—is to commit a fraud on our children. If the children were as astute as their elders supposedly are they would say: "I'm sorry, but I'm not ever going to be ten years old again. Can't you afford to give me good teachers *now?*"

The elementary and high schools would have to enlarge their teaching staffs by at least five hundred thousand in the next ten years merely to maintain the present pupil-teacher ratio; this is a greater increase than took place in the previous thirty-five years. To achieve this net increase of 500,000 three times that many will have to be recruited to take care of those who leave to get married, to take other jobs, or retire. The colleges and universities will have to add more teachers in the next fifteen years than they have in all their previous history.

In this formidable and unprecedented situation we are faced with a long-standing shortage of about one hundred forty thousand qualified teachers. More than half the college graduates will have to enter the teaching profession during the next ten years if our schools are to be adequately staffed. At present only one fifth of the college graduates become teachers. In fact, many who plan to become teachers decide after graduation that the rewards are too meager. This is particularly true in the fields most needed in a technological society—mathematics and science. There the supply of prospective teachers has been dropping steadily. For example, from 4,618 college graduates prepared to teach mathematics in 1950 the figure dropped to 2,892 in 1957, of whom only two thirds actually went into teaching. The respective figures for science are 9,096 in 1950 and 5,044 in 1957, again with only about two thirds entering the teaching profession. Incredible as it may sound, a mere 125 prospective physics teachers graduated in 1955 to be fought over by some 28,000 high schools. Despite competition for their services nothing has been done to grant better salaries to teachers with such rare qualifications.

In the third field of importance today—foreign languages— the situation is even more serious. One consequence is that we have a diplomatic service where only 50 per cent now have command of a foreign language and where—still worse —a mere 30 per cent of the incoming recruits speak any foreign language; clear evidence of the deterioration of foreign-language teaching in the last generation.

At a time when the United States has commitments all over the world we have only one ambassador in a communist country who speaks the language; in the Near East and North Africa, among the most critical areas of world politics today, only two of our ambassadors speak Arabic. The situation is no better for our diplomatic dealings with the North Atlantic Treaty nations. As of March 1958 our ambassadors to Belgium, France, Germany, Iceland, the Netherlands, Portugal, Turkey, and Greece did not have a workable knowledge of the language of their host countries. I venture to say that such linguistic deficiencies cannot be found in the foreign service of any other leading power in the world.

A recent UNESCO study of foreign-language teaching in fourteen selected countries showed the United States near the bottom of the list in spite of the fact that we have a built-in linguistic advantage in our immigrants from many lands. We make little use of this advantage; our mores have no use for immigrant bilingualism—a potential source of future language teachers such as few other countries possess.

A would-be teacher would have to spend many years of intensive study to acquire proficiency in an unknown foreign language. This would get him no higher financial reward than that earned by a teacher with identical degree and seniority who teaches driver training, domestic science, or typewriting. Can anyone seriously maintain that it is democratic to single out teaching from all other occupations for such allegedly "democratic" salary scales where merit counts for nothing and the relative difficulty of the subject taught is considered irrelevant? It is not surprising that our teacher shortage is most severe among those teaching academic subjects who merit far higher salaries. Understandably, the shortage is less among those who teach simple "know-how" subjects and who probably merit no more than what they actually earn. As is the case with college professors, a teacher of mathematics, science, or foreign languages has many opportunities to make a good living outside of teaching, whereas the teacher of print shop or fly casting would probably not do so well elsewhere. The able teachers leave and the less able remain. The best is never cheap. We have been getting our children's education at bargain rates, as Columbia's President Grayson Kirk remarked—at cut rates "subsidized by those who could least afford it: the teachers" —and the quality of education has been affected by our failure to reward excellence in teaching.

Chapter 7

THE EDUCATION OF
OUR TALENTED YOUTH

A specific aspect of the crisis in American education is the failure of the schools to identify and develop our talented youth. The waste of this, our most precious national asset, results in a loss to the nation which we can ill afford. It shows up in our chronic shortages of highly trained professional people—a problem known to leaders in education, government, and industry for some time, although the general public has been slow to perceive it. Only in the last few years have we begun to realize that our shortage of trained man power is the inevitable consequence of a long-term trend in American education which must be halted if we wish to retain our technological lead. To put it bluntly, our schools do not perform their primary purpose, which is to train the nation's brain power to its highest potential.

One half of our children who are endowed with the ability to enter college and university do not do so. For every high-school graduate who eventually earns a doctoral degree there are twenty-five others who have the mental capacity to achieve that degree but do not. Lack of funds is only partly responsible for this irreplaceable loss. Had there been proper motivation, nearly all of these young people could have found ways and means to obtain a professional education, and we would not be faced today with a deficiency of trained man power.

This is a serious indictment of our schools. It is a defect in American education which cannot be entirely blamed on inadequate school funds though it is sometimes aggravated by lack of money. The fault for neglecting our talented children lies in deep-seated national attitudes and in faulty edu-

111

cational theories and practices. Unless these are changed, the much-needed contributions of many potential scientists, engineers, or other professional persons will be lost. There are not enough young people with above-average minds and we cannot spare any of them. We must make special provision for our talented children. Every American has a legitimate concern with our educational system. Our children are the nation's hostages to the future. Both as parents and as citizens we have no more important job than to insure that all are given the very best education they are capable of absorbing. Never has this been more important than today when we are in danger of being outdistanced in technological developments by Russia.

It is unfortunate that our social mores are hostile to acceptance of the fact that children have unequal mental abilities and therefore learn at different speeds and cannot all climb equally high on the ladder of education; or that children grow up in diverse kinds of homes which vary greatly in the emphasis of respect for learning and absorb a sense of obligation to improve their capabilities, while others grow up in families not interested in education. Obviously, the former will be more strongly motivated toward exerting an effort to do well in school.

The Declaration of Independence declares that all men are born equal but the Lord has seen fit to give us minds that differ in capacity to absorb formal education. The mind is not the sole criterion of a person's human effectiveness and value. We all know people who cannot master mathematics or understand Shakespeare's plays but who are whizzes at practical things. We know people who are not very intelligent but whose hearts are as big as all outdoors. Who is to say that they are less worth-while when what is lacking in the head is balanced by what comes from the heart? The infinite variety of his kind is the glory of man. Lesser creatures are born identical—ants look alike and seem to do their jobs with equal efficiency. They are assuredly well adjusted to their "peer" group. Some of our schools remind one of busy anthills. In fact, Senator Flanders of Vermont calls ours a "happy ant-school system" and warns that history gives us little cause to feel confident that a happy, cooperative ant society will survive. When we try to treat children as if they were as identical as ants and therefore able to absorb the same schooling, we go against nature; against the incontrovertible fact that in any representative group of children a spread of several years in mental age between the slowest and fastest learner appears as early as the second grade. By age twelve this spread may have become six years.

In our society all men are considered equal as human beings and as children of God; they are also equal as citizens. All are entitled to justice in the courts which, put another way, means equality before the law. All have the right to an equal vote in choosing the men who govern us. All deserve equal respect for honest work, whether it be simple or complicated. Many kinds of work are necessary to make our society function properly. Each is useful and of value. But intellectually we are not equal. We disregard this fact at our peril. We harm the nation and our children when we force them all into the strait jacket of the comprehensive school without making very careful provisions for homogeneous grouping.

This is difficult to do because popular opinion frowns upon giving special consideration to talented children in tax-supported schools. To recognize inequality of intellectual ability is repugnant to our egalitarian philosophy. We are firmly committed to the assumption that in our democratic society no person can claim to be an *indispensable man*. We proceed from this entirely correct assumption to the incorrect conclusion that neither does our society have *indispensable men*. This is obviously erroneous. A moment's reflection will show that no society can function without its indispensable men. By this I mean the men who because of natural endowment and careful training possess the intellectual, artistic, and moral abilities to build upon existing foundations and to carry forward the momentum of civilization. It has been estimated that the efforts of less than one per cent of the total population move the world forward. This small group is indispensable to the maintenance and advancement of our civilization.

No nation has ever had too many indispensable men. In primitive handicraft societies a handful suffices; more are needed in civilized societies. The more complex a society becomes, the larger proportionately the number of intelligent, highly trained men who are needed for its proper functioning. They are the men who provide leadership in government, industry, and labor; the men who think creatively, who invent, who push the boundaries of knowledge outward; the men who enrich life through their moral leadership or artistic gifts—the many competent people who manage our complex technological civilization. They are all indispensable to our society. We must keep their ranks replenished by a continuous inflow of properly trained youth of superior mental ability if we are to progress in the future as we have in the past.

Three years ago the Research and Development Subcommittee of the Joint Atomic Energy Committee of the Congress conducted protracted hearings into the problem of shortage of scientific and engineering man power. A procession of outstanding scientists and engineers and many leaders in other fields of intellectual endeavor testified before the committee. No one can read this testimony and maintain the glib optimism which unfortunately animates so many of the men in American education. The total inadequacy of our public education is manifest on every page of this volume of hearings. Our foolish neglect of the nation's best brains comes out time and time again. It would be prudent to take the committee's own words seriously. Expressing the hope that the published hearings may provide a basis for constructive action and that our citizens, especially the parents of the coming generation, will join in such action, the committee warns that there are no easy solutions but that "it has . . . become apparent that the shortage of scientific and engineering talent is only part of a much larger national problem of identifying and developing our best young minds in this country so as to realize maximum advantage from our potential intellectual resources. It is the development of this brain power and the upgrading of our educational system so as to make it more attuned to the needs of our economy which is at once the most challenging and most important job we have to do."

Although the committee was concerned primarily with the man-power shortage delaying our atomic-energy program, its members declared that "it has become increasingly obvious that in the long run an adequate number of trained technicians for atomic energy can best be achieved, and maintained, *by increasing our over-all supply of specialized talent in all fields of endeavor.*" It must be said that the committee's hope of concerted action by citizens and educational institutions has not been realized. Three years have gone by. Russia has not stood still. The longer we dally; the longer we refuse to admit our mistakes; the longer we permit a pressure group interested in the educational *status quo* to stifle reform; the longer we delay upgrading our educational system, the harder will it be to overcome Russia's technological lead in certain important fields. Certainly the most effective step we can take immediately is to unshackle our talented youth from the lock step of the average and below-average pupil who is forced to or wishes only to have fun at school. We still have time to make a choice. Unless we abandon false "democratic" clichés which interpret democracy as enthronement of the commonplace and obstruction of excellence, we may find that we have traded democratic freedom for a mess of pseudo-democratic mediocrity. It is not difficult to imagine what this may mean to the future position of the United States in world affairs.

Today technological progress is limited only by availability of trained professionals, and this, in turn, depends on but two factors: incidence of superior brain power—over which we have little, if any, control; and development of available talent—here we can do much. Who, then, are our

talented youth, and what provisions are we making for their
intellectual training?

There is no general agreement on the definition of the
term "talented." Sometimes it is applied only to the top 1½
to 2 per cent of our children—those with an I.Q. of 135 and
over. At other times it is given wider application to take in
all who are above the average of high-school graduates, i.e.,
110 I.Q. and over.

A few figures may help to give perspective. The average
intelligence of the total population has been arbitrarily set
at 100; on this basis, those who enter high school average
105; those who graduate from high school, 110; those who
enter college, 115; and college graduates, 120. Generalized
classifications such as these tend to be arbitrary, and I.Q.
tests are not infallible. Moreover, they leave out of consideration differences in character and in will power. A lazy
child with a high I.Q. may well be outstripped at school
and later on in life by a child with a lower I.Q. but with
drive and motivation.

If we wish to include potential late bloomers and children
who are exceptionally motivated, we may put the percentage
of those who can readily absorb a college-preparatory course
at about 15 to 20 per cent. This includes all with an I.Q. of
115 and above. For comparison, 15 per cent of English
children are able to pass the entrance examinations to the
now tuition-free upper-track secondary schools (called
grammar schools). Not all of these complete the course and
only about one half or so enter universities to train for
professional careers. European educators have had much
experience with the capabilities of talented children; something which is lacking in this country. Their governments
must select carefully for they cannot afford to waste tax
money for higher education on children who simply cannot
profit from it. Since we are richer, we might consider taking
greater chances and set the number who should be strongly
urged to take rigorous college-preparatory courses at 20 per
cent or perhaps even 25 per cent. This would include children who can complete such a program only if they study

very hard and are strongly supported in this endeavor by both home and school.[1]

At present very little is done in our schools to seek out and identify our talented children. In most schools they are being taught along with the 80 per cent of average and below-average mentality, although there is some selection through the elective system. Only those with good minds are apt to take the academic college-preparatory program. Unfortunately, not nearly enough of those who can master such a program actually select it. Very little provision is currently being made to take into consideration the fact that talented children learn much faster than others. Consequently, the length of time spent in school is the same for almost all children.

There is ample evidence that in any class which includes slow and fast learners the slower group sets the pace and receives more attention from the teacher. The above-average children are kept from advancing at the speed appropriate to their ability, with the result that some lose interest in learning as such, others develop sloppy habits, and a few build up a false sense of superiority which convinces them that they are so smart that they will never need to apply themselves to anything. The deadly routine sets in on these young and malleable minds.

Talented children whose minds are not challenged become frustrated and often turn into poor pupils from sheer boredom. Mental muscles become flabby if the child's mind is not constantly being strained to the utmost. The mind is no different from any other part of the body. It deteriorates when it isn't used for its proper purpose—to *think*.

As is often the case, where there is community pressure not to fail the poor student, advancement into the next higher grade becomes virtually automatic. This tends to convince the slow learners and lazy pupils that they can get by without working. Talented children may well resent having to work harder for no tangible reward. All children

---

[1] For greater percentage of children enrolled in academic programs in Russia, see Chapter 9 and Appendix 3.

need incentives to keep up the learning process. Therefore, the practice which is to be found in many schools of "never giving A's," or of "grading the child only as against his own past performance," or of limiting report-card comments to "satisfactory" and "needs improvement" is pernicious; it is a particularly unfortunate concession to the sensibilities of parents whose children show neither ability nor a desire to learn.

In the ideal well-adjusted group which the died-in-the-wool educationist is determined to create, the talented child is a misfit. Educationists are wont to call him a "fortunate deviate" or an "exceptional child"—in that peculiar pedagogic meaning of the term which implies that he ranks with "the mentally and physically handicapped, persons with impaired sight, hearing, and speech, and those with pronounced problems of adjustment," who all require special facilities. Such terminology is oddly revealing of American educationist thinking which seems to look upon the talented child primarily as a vexing administrative problem. In contrast, there are few European teachers—even in the smallest village elementary school—who are not constantly on the lookout for the bright child and who will not make every effort to push him up the educational ladder as far and fast as he will go.

Although he is ranked with physically handicapped children, the talented child is less adequately served in American schools. Of course we must and should make special provision for unfortunate children. Our hearts are here involved, and it is to the credit of Americans that they will readily abandon such cherished principles as "equal education for all" to answer the call of compassion. Yet why should we show less compassion for the mentally superior child whose fine abilities are being left untended?

The majority of high-school pupils have no taste for the college-preparatory program which alone is appropriate to the needs and abilities of talented children. For the non-academically inclined, the schools therefore provide a multitude of easy courses which demand neither mental exertion nor homework. Some educationists consider homework altogether unnecessary and even perhaps harmful. Because the high school tries to be all things to all children, it must necessarily operate on the elective system. Few children— even talented children—have so earnest a love of learning, such intellectual fortitude, as to pass up the chance to coast through school on easy vocational, recreational, or sheerly trivial subjects. Unless wisely guided by parents and teachers, they will elect the easiest and most pleasant school subjects. Indeed this is what many have long been doing.

We expect too much of children when we leave the planning of their study program to their own discretion. The schools apparently do not accept the legal concept of the "minor" who must be protected by society from making decisions which will harm him. The law in all civilized countries recognizes that children under twenty-one (or in some cases under eighteen) lack the experience and wisdom to determine the course of their future lives. The minor may not marry, or purchase intoxicating liquor, or sell his property. He may not expatriate himself from his native country, but in our schools the minor is allowed to elect courses which may expatriate him from the realm of higher learning. Talented children are often slower to decide on their careers since their interests are broad and they are more versatile than the average child. Withal, they are children and ought not be burdened with the responsibility of planning their own education.

Quite apart from the damage done to our talented children by the elective system, the absence of a definitive, well-thought-out liberal-arts program continuing over at least six years has the undesirable effect of making our whole educational system unresponsive to changing national needs for particular kinds of professional people. It may sound paradoxical, but the very lack of definitive school programs makes for greater rigidity in our system, compared to that prevailing in the leading European nations. Students enrolled in the academic secondary schools abroad receive a general education, so broadly founded in the humanities and sciences that they can at age eighteen choose almost any professional course of study. A sudden change in national demand from, say, French linguists to nuclear physicists or to theoretical mathematicians can therefore be met within the prescribed period of *professional* preparation—roughly four years. In this country, on the other hand, many a bright youngster may have made a poor choice of his high-school program, selecting the easy courses and neglecting mathematics, sciences, and languages. At eighteen he is therefore unprepared for professional careers demanding fundamental knowledge in these subjects. No matter how promising such careers may have become in the interim, no matter how greatly the young man may now be interested in one of these careers, they are in effect barred to him.

Fundamentals in the liberal arts must be learned in high school. Time lost there can seldom be made up. There is a limit to the number of years a student can spend at a school desk. Professional training takes more and more years as professional skill and knowledge increase, and therefore the short time in man's life when his mind can best absorb knowledge and lay the foundation of a liberal education must not be wasted on trivialities such as photography, woodshop, or retail selling. It is incredible how mistaken young people often are about their future needs and how inadequately they are counseled. A classic story is one told by President Griswold of Yale. A boy applying for admission submitted the following high-school credits: two in English, one in American history, and the remaining nine credits in the following subjects: typing, speech, chorus, physical education, journalism, personality problems, and marriage and family. It would be funny were it not so deeply tragic. Anyone my age must remember that in our own youth high schools did not send such ill-equipped youngsters into the world. This young man at eighteen was still so uninformed about his educational needs that he believed this kind of high-school program gave him a chance to enter Yale! There are, unfortunately, some colleges that will accept him and let him continue to pursue "practical" subjects and finally give him an academic degree, but does anyone believe that the boy really received an education above the elementary and vocational level? This sort of thing is all too frequent under our system and makes a mockery of educationist boasting that we give the best education to the most children of any country in the world.

Apart from foisting on our children a shabby substitute for good higher schooling, the inelasticity of our school system delays vitally needed work for lack of professionals. In today's rapidly spiraling technological civilization it is essential that the educational system be sufficiently elastic to permit quick shifts from one profession to another as demand changes. In this country such shifts are delayed for from eight to twelve years because there must be a shift not only in professional training but in high-school and sometimes in college programs as well.

This inelasticity is the price we pay for the "democratic benefits" supposedly derived by forcing all children—below-average, average, talented, and brilliant—to march together to their eighteenth year, absorbing lots of life adjustment but so little real education that it takes another four years in a liberal-arts college to complete the broad general education needed by future professional people.

It is true that of late the needs of our talented children have won some recognition, but so far recognition has been confined to a small segment of the population. Not yet won is the mass support necessary to bring about truly effective measures by legislature bodies, from which must come the necessary laws and financial contributions to upgrade the schooling of talented youth. We are still in the early stages of isolated studies, tentative experiments in a few localities, and long-drawn arguments pro and con. More important, American public thinking has not yet connected shortages of trained man power with inadequate provision for the proper education of the talented. Nor are we sufficiently aware that, in final analysis, our cherished American standard of living depends on the work of a relatively small group of skilled professionals.

To some extent this is a consequence of a curious inconsistency in our attitude toward "science" as against "scientists" and "scholars." We admire "science" greatly and we place in it an almost childlike trust; we expect it will continuously pour out delightful wonders to make our lives ever more agreeable. But upon "scientists" and "scholars" many of us look with a somewhat jaundiced eye; we call them "eggheads" and "intellectuals"; we do not consider them to be entirely normal persons. In truth, we have no real admiration for higher learning as such, nor are we willing to respect those engaged in it unless we see an immediate practical advantage to ourselves in their work. Most Americans dislike the very idea that some people are more brilliant than others though they are ready enough to recognize inequality of natural endowment in other respects. This negative attitude toward the mentally superior is surprising when we compare it with the generous applause lavished on superior talent in athletics or in the arts; on superior beauty or on business acumen.

However, as I mentioned, a beginning has now been made toward understanding mentally superior children. The bright child has been put under the microscope; he has been studied, measured, and observed. Our knowledge of his capacities and needs has been somewhat increased. For example, Professor Terman's studies with a group of youngsters having high I.Q.'s verify certain factors long suspected by those dealing with gifted children. They are usually as superior physically as they are mentally. The comforting folk myth that if they have brains they are undersize or spindly ought now to be discarded together with black cats and knocking on wood. Intelligent children are, as a rule, more cheerful and emotionally more stable than others. This is so, of course, only if their intellectual progress has not been too severely hampered; otherwise, frustration may bring about boredom and irritability, thereby upsetting their emotional equilibrium. Possibly "adjustment" to the age group is more than one can expect of a child who is several years mentally ahead of the group.

Even with inadequate provisions for their specific educational needs, a test group of 1,000 brilliant children did remarkably well. As compared with average high-school graduates, ten times as many went to college and on to postgraduate work; sixteen times as many made Phi Beta Kappa; twenty times as many became lawyers or physicians; and more than sixty times as many had either earned a Ph.D. degree or were well on the way toward achieving it.

Although not all bright children are academically inclined, enough of them do so well at institutions of higher learning that spending public funds for better education of *all* talented youth is an exceedingly good investment for the nation as a whole, and would do much to relieve our national deficit in trained professionals.

Relatively few concrete measures are being taken to provide appropriate schooling for these youngsters. Most programs are, in my opinion, quite inadequate for one or more of these reasons:

First, they deal only with the brilliant child of 135 I.Q. and over, leaving untouched the needs of the far larger group of *talented* children. Little encouragement is given the ambitious student whose I.Q. rating is perhaps no more than high average but who is determined on a professional career and *wants* to put in effort to complete his education as fast as possible. If anything, such children are discouraged in the United States. They would normally go through the upper-track secondary school abroad and complete their professional studies several years earlier; proof positive that this can be done, given enough drive.

Second, few programs take into account the fact that talented children get through their schooling much faster than the average child. This ability seems to be resented as giving an unfair advantage to the talented minority which ought not to be allowed in a democratic school. Quite exaggerated concern is also felt for talented children who might have social problems if they were allowed to move through school more rapidly than the rest of the children. It has always seemed to me that common sense would indicate that a bright child would have less trouble adjusting to older children whose mental age is near his own, than to children with the same chronological age who are years behind him mentally. The whole problem is an artificial one and arises from our insistence that all children must go to the same type of school; it hardly exists in Europe, where schools are kept small and homogeneous.

Third, most programs are not bold enough because, for the reason given above, they seek solutions within our existing all-inclusive school system. Multiple tracks are about the best way this can be done and fortunately they are slowly being accepted. Many programs, however, offer merely "enrichment" or "individual acceleration." Both are poor substitutes for a carefully thought-out academic program covering at least six years from the seventh to the twelfth grade. All talented children in Europe benefit from such a program. As Arthur Bestor writes, "A trustworthy concept of equal educational opportunities must rest upon a broader base than the experience of a single nation. Young Americans are not being offered genuine equality of opportunity unless they can obtain what young men and women elsewhere are receiving." By clinging to the notion that separate schools for talented youth are unacceptable in this country, we make a great deal of unnecessary trouble for ourselves. I venture to say that the majority of America's best young minds are seldom challenged at school and spend many hours of acute boredom during that period of their lives when they could easily absorb a great deal of knowledge and sharpen their minds.

As practiced in most schools, "enrichment" is the very opposite of what the talented child needs. He can grasp ideas rapidly and does not need to spend extra enriched time going over and over the same subject. What he needs is to be allowed to pass on rapidly to the next idea, a process which inevitably takes him quickly far beyond the program pursued by slower learners. This he is seldom permitted to do. Too often enrichment becomes a sort of "make-work" or "make-study" project to keep the smart children occupied with time-consuming tasks that are just as boring to them as the non-enriched program offered to the rest of the class.

We must give more weight to this factor of speed in dealing with our talented. It might come as a surprise just how fast they can learn. Dr. Hollingworth found that children of an I.Q. of 135 and above actually could complete the requirements of the curriculum prescribed for the public school of New York City in as little as one quarter of the time needed by average pupils. Dr. Meister, long head of the splendid Bronx High School of Science, remarked before the Senate Committee on Labor and Public Welfare: "Things that I would take two or three periods to explain in the average school would be done here in five minutes." After giving an astonishing example, he went to the very heart of the matter with these remarks: "You do not get that kind of learning unless you bring good minds together. The impact of good mind upon good mind raises the sights, and raises the standards, and gives you the kind of excellence that I think we need in this day and age." The Bronx High School of Science is a four-year high school to which only brilliant students are admitted. The program is challenging and much college-level work is done there. Its primary purpose does not seem to be acceleration.

New York City used to have a three-year high school for brilliant children which had a long and honorable history of more than eighty years. The Townsend Harris School graduated its students at least a year ahead of those in other city high schools. When the school was abolished in 1942, one reason given was that such acceleration was both "undemocratic" and harmful since the boys were too young when they entered college. Efforts are now being made to reactivate this school.

"Individual acceleration" used to be much more common before the life-adjustment people took over. Determined parents can still get some schools to let their bright children advance rather than have them lose all interest in studies from sheer boredom, but it takes a deal of doing. But individual acceleration is only a second-best solution for the talented. At best, the child misses part of the curriculum and he still does not find the mental stimulation he would experience in a class with equally talented children. Though older, his new classmates are still slower learners; they are mentally not his "peers."

Some communities do try to provide schooling appropriate to their gifted children. A few of our largest cities have special high schools with an exclusively academic curriculum; Central High School and Girls' High School in Philadelphia, for example. These draw pupils from the whole city and will not retain anyone who cannot meet their relatively high scholastic standards; those who fail are returned to the regular high school of their district. New York City has at present two four-year high schools for brilliant children, the Bronx High School of Science for boys and Hunter High for girls. These accept pupils from the whole city but screen out all but the brilliant.

Some schools maintain gifted-children programs of high scholastic standing within an otherwise regular comprehensive high school. The two Philadelphia schools mentioned above have special gifted programs. So has the New Trier Township High School in Winnetka, Illinois. There is also a program for gifted children in Palo Alto, California, in which the entire school system—twenty elementary, two junior and two senior high schools—participates. This program involves 1,500 talented children, or 15 per cent of the total school population of 10,000. I am not personally familiar with this program but I understand that it permits acceleration.

Resistance to acceleration among many educationists perpetuates for most of our talented youth the slow pace of American preprofessional education. There is no valid reason why our bright children should be forever forced to trail Europeans by two to three years. However, some slight progress is finally being made toward lopping off at least one year from the sixteen-year elementary high-school-liberal-arts college sequence. A number of colleges and high schools are now cooperating in the Advanced Placement Program which grew out of a joint study by three colleges and three preparatory schools and is presently being administered by the College Entrance Examination Board. Briefly, the program works like this: selected high schools undertake to offer college-level courses to carefully selected students of high ability. If these pass the examinations of the college board, the cooperating colleges will usually give advanced standing to such students and in some few cases permit them to complete college a year earlier. There are a number of other experiments now going on which aim to give high-school students a chance to take tougher courses and skip the freshman year. This is all to the good, but I think it does not go far enough.

A great deal of time is wasted in elementary school. It is now widely admitted that children abroad come to grips with the tools of learning far sooner than do our children. Talented children can easily be advanced at the beginning of their school life when home tutoring presents no difficulties. Thus another year could be cut off during the first six grades in addition to a possible year cut off from college. Bright children would then be able to get through their preprofessional studies in fourteen years. Even then they will be a little older than their European contemporaries.

It is high time that we give belated recognition to the special educational requirements of talented youth. Provision for the needs of the average and the below-average, as well as the physically handicapped, has long ago been made. It must always be remembered that the transformation of the traditionally academic American high school into a combination college-preparatory, vocational, and social institution came about in response to demand for schooling appropriate to the majority of children—those who could not or did not want to take academic courses but whose parents nevertheless wished them to attend high school. As nonacademic, know-how subjects wormed themselves into the curriculum, the high school was less and less able to give proper attention to the special educational needs of the minority of children whose superior intellect could find no challenge in downgraded curricula. This is particularly true in small communities where the college-preparatory program of the high school is apt to suffer whenever shortages of school funds or teachers occur, as at present. We shall not do justice to these children until we seek them out at an early age and educate them separately. This need not necessarily be in a special school; it could be in a college preparatory section of the comprehensive school. But separate schooling should begin with the sixth or seventh grade. The curriculum should be purely academic, and the teachers should have professional competence in the subjects they teach. Admission as well as advancement into each higher grade should be by examination. If possible, the school year should be extended to 210 days. There is no other country of comparable civilization where children go to school for only 180 days.

We would never dream of putting the star athlete, the child of average athletic aptitude, and the physically handicapped child in the same physical-education class, on the same playing field, or on the same team. This is what we now do with children of correspondingly different mental aptitudes. I have heard of many a star athlete who obtains his diploma despite manifest scholastic failure but I have yet to hear of the "A" student who is made a member of the baseball team despite manifest athletic failure. If one is democratic, why not the other?

With all the talk about how unfair it would be to give special schooling to the talented, it may not be amiss to point out that this would at any rate not need to cost much more than average schooling. In some cases it might even cost less. Some schools provide costly vocational and recreational paraphernalia for the majority of children who take know-how courses. In such schools a gifted-children program might well cost less, for it needs no expensive equipment except a science laboratory. The principal item in such a program would be the cost of a psychological testing service to locate talent; well-trained and inspired teachers—if they can be found—cost no more than teachers of vocational subjects with the same academic degrees; they cost less, incidentally, than athletic coaches! Deplorable as this is from the standpoint of rewarding teachers properly for excellence of training and performance, it would be advantageous to our talented youth who need every opportunity they can get.

The Palo Alto program for gifted children costs an extra $52,000 for 1,500 pupils, or $34.66 per child annually. Compare this with the cost of $57,500 for a special program involving 75 mentally defective children. This is to be expected, since much effort and equipment must go into helping handicapped children and of course nobody begrudges money so spent. The contrast in what can be done with bright children for a tiny fraction of the money lavished on mentally defective children is nevertheless astonishing.

I am aware that any change in the American public-school system will meet opposition. Special schooling for the mentally superior will be branded as "undemocratic" and as "class" education. It will be considered "unfair" to give the talented child education superior to that offered the average child. It will be said that separation of children according to mental capacity denies them the valuable experience of living together with other children of varied background and ability; that they will therefore miss training, which constitutes an important ingredient in the smooth functioning of American democracy—so it will be said. None of these objections, however, bear critical examination.

Education is not a commodity such as a house, a television set, or an automobile. Everyone can use and enjoy a house, a TV set, or a car; it would indeed be "unfair" if the state distributed these commodities free of charge but limited them to a small section of the population. The ability to use and enjoy academic training, on the other hand, is not universal; therefore, to limit it to those who can benefit from it is not unfair; but to deny it to the minority who *can* use and derive benefit from academic training is both unfair and undemocratic, as well as a waste of our most valuable national asset.

As to the objection that the experience of democratic living will be lost if the talented are separated, this again would be true only if all bright children came from the same type of home. As long as pupils in *all* public schools, including those giving college preparatory courses, are drawn from the whole population and all students are given the same opportunity to advance according to their ability, the social values of learning to live among children of varying backgrounds will still be preserved.

It would, indeed, be "undemocratic" to propose a cleavage along class lines, but not one along the lines of natural ability, which hardly anyone will claim is limited to children coming from better homes. It is often forgotten that we already have just such a separation along class lines in large American cities where schools draw their pupils from a particular neighborhood rather than from the whole population, as is the case in smaller towns. Neighborhoods in America are usually homogeneous, at least as far as the finances of families are concerned. Parents in better-class neighborhoods generally succeed in obtaining better schools for their children. Finally, we must not forget that well-to-do parents always have it in their power to assure their children a good education by sending them to private preparatory schools. But the talented poor child must depend on the public school. Education in a democracy must not only be democratic, it must also be education.

Chapter 8

MASS EDUCATION AND MERIT

The student who wishes to become a professional person in this country must invest more time and more money in the preparation for his career than his contemporaries in the advanced nations of Europe. Our professional education, in general, is good, but it is severely handicapped by the weakness of our public elementary and secondary education. Elsewhere twelve years of schooling are sufficient to teach students to read and to write the mother tongue correctly; to obtain a solid foundation in history, geography, mathematics, and the sciences; and to acquire competence in reading at least two foreign languages. Upon this foundation professional schools design programs of three to five years' duration to equip an already broadly educated young man or woman with the vast fund of specialized knowledge required by a modern professional person.

Now if the underpinning is weak, as in America, two things must happen: either the future professional must lengthen his period of schooling by two to four years in a liberal-arts college, prior to professional study, so that he may acquire sufficient general knowledge to perform his professional duties in a wise and socially responsible manner, or professional study itself must be overloaded with remedial courses and with hastily concocted general humanities courses to patch up the gaps in his preprofessional schooling.

In the first case, the time required to attain professional standing is lengthened beyond what is tolerable to many talented young people—they simply will not wait that long to establish themselves and become economically independ-

131

ent. Moreover, having to attend college before starting professional school is costly for the student as well as for the college. There is first the expense of room and board—an item absent in the cost of a European professional education since the whole of preprofessional general education is covered in secondary schools with students living at home. Then, tuition for college runs about one thousand to fifteen hundred annually for the student [1] and as much again for the college since today students pay on an average only half of what it costs the college to educate them. On top of all this comes the cost of the subsequent professional education.

In the second case, where completion of a college education is not made mandatory for all students wishing to enter a professional school, the professional school will attempt to make up for the deficiencies in elementary and secondary education. This sometimes means remedial work on a student's spelling and grammar; remedial mathematics is very common for engineering students. Time spent on preprofessional education is lost to professional education. The first two years in engineering schools, for example, lean heavily to basic courses in mathematics and sciences which most Europeans take in secondary school. The result is that in this country too much of the engineering course proper must be squeezed into the last two years. The study load becomes burdensome—about sixty hours a week of classroom, laboratory, and homework for four years. The student achieves only a sketchy sort of liberal education, and such cramming is not the best preparation for a profession.

The chronic shortage of good scientists, engineers, and other professionals which plagues us is largely the result of inadequate preprofessional education—of time wasted in public school which somehow must be made up later on.

It is said that our public education must concern itself more with the average students who do not wish to become doctors, lawyers, or engineers. For these average students the situation is, if anything, worse. They must depend for

[1] In state universities, this cost is borne by the taxpayer.

competence in dealing with life's problems on what they have learned in the twelve years from age six to eighteen.

This is the time in a youngster's life when he can most easily absorb large numbers of facts and when his curiosity can be most readily stimulated to want to do so. This is the time when young minds should be filled to capacity with impressions; when they should be stretched to their maximum. Only the school can do this. It can do it for children of most varied natural endowments if it frankly recognizes these variations and devises curricula tailored to the capacities of the talented, the average, and the below-average child. Each group can then develop best at its own rate of speed. The same basic process of storing the mind with knowledge can be adapted for each group of students.

The above-average pupil who is from two to three years *ahead* of the average in mental age is able to move through the elementary and secondary schools in that much less time, given the chance to do so in a homogeneous group. The below-average child who may be an equal number of years *behind* the average in mental age will need longer. It may often be possible for him to absorb no more than is offered in the first eight grades and he may not be able to cover this before he is sixteen. But although he learns more slowly and cannot go so far as children with better minds, he, too, needs to be taught to think and to use the basic intellectual tools without which he would be helpless in today's world. With care and patience he can be taught at least the three "R's," and he ought never to be rushed into vocational training at the cost of learning these three minimum requirements of civilized life. The educational process for all children must be one of absorbing knowledge to the limit of their capacity. Recreation, manual or clerical training, etiquette, and similar know-how subjects have little effect on the mind itself, and it is with the mind that the school must solely concern itself. The poorer a child's natural endowments the more he needs to have his mind trained.

Our elementary and secondary education should thus provide first, for the average and below-average student, a sufficiently broad terminal education to fit him into a modern technological society; and second, for the talented student, a solid base for subsequent professional education. Neither of these two objectives is achieved in the majority of American public schools.

Why do most of our public schools fail in the objectives I have mentioned? One reason is that we are wedded in this country to the concept of the comprehensive school. The administrative difficulties of combining several different study programs simultaneously in a single institution are great. The schools which have done it with some success have used the multiple-track system. This was frowned upon by many educators and parents until very recently. The following is perhaps a somewhat extreme case of parental disapproval though I myself heard of a parallel case occurring last year in a school attended by children of friends. A young high-school principal, after testing his pupils, found that he had enough talented students to warrant setting up a special course for them—a tough academic curriculum. The children liked it and so did their parents; not the rest of the community. Furious at what they considered "unfair" treatment of their own children, the parents of those not included in the hard course not only managed to get it stopped but got rid of the young principal to boot.

The comprehensive secondary school is a uniquely American institution, an outgrowth of the post-Jacksonian upsurge of democracy. It is the concrete expression of an ideal of one free school attended by all American children, rich and poor, native and foreign-born, of one faith or another—all growing up together, learning to get along with each other, absorbing democratic habits and ideals as by osmosis. This ideal runs smack into the incontrovertible fact that children are unequally endowed with intelligence and determination and that it is impossible to educate the slow, average, and fast learners together if by educating we mean development of the capacity to think, to understand, and to make wise decisions. When the great inflow into our high schools began early in this century, some 80 per cent of the pupils could not or would not "take" the regular secondary-school curriculum. Heretofore secondary schools had taught liberal-arts subjects —the humanities and the sciences. Theirs was an intellectually more rigorous curriculum than that of elementary and vocational schools. The American ideal of free universal education through high school originated in the belief that secondary-school education was of value to the development of *all* children and that none should be barred from it by the cost of tuition. At that time little was known of the differences in intellectual endowments; I.Q. tests had not yet been invented. We did not know that aptitude for learning above the elementary level was relatively rare. When this was a pioneering country, intellectual inequality could not be easily observed. In fact, the practical man of courage and physical strength was more successful than the intellectual when both of them were engaged in taming the wilderness. Americans are extremely reluctant to admit that we are intellectually unequal. We were even less able to accept this fact fifty years ago.

When the majority of pupils rejected the regular secondary-school curriculum, we did not set up an alternative program for them, leaving the academic course to pupils destined for the professions and other careers that require a broad liberal education. We kept pupils together and tried to provide for different educational needs by the elective system. In order to preserve the ideal of comprehensive schooling, we established compulsory "core" programs for all students. These demanded so little mental effort that everyone could attend. They were supposed to help young people with practical problems of daily life. Emphasis was on the needs of the majority while scant attention was given to the talented minority. This seemingly democratic procedure preserved equality of education *literally* but abolished it *in fact*. What might have been of some use to the majority often was of no use whatever to the talented few.

In order to "hold" children in school until their late teens, we drifted into abandonment of standards of excellence throughout our educational system. All children have suffered in consequence. Our schools fail in the basic objective of giving each child a good education because this has long since ceased to be the real objective of American public education. True there was mass pressure to downgrade curricula which the majority of children could not master, but it must be said that the leaders of education did not defend scholastic standards. They gave up too easily when pupils resisted the tough academic subjects. Perhaps it was inevitable. Certainly it would have taken courage and infinite patience to "sell" the value of a true secondary education to the majority of pupils and their parents. In this difficulty the theories of John Dewey offered an easy escape, and our educational leaders went over to him en masse. His emphasis on fitting curricula to the desires and interests of children, his deprecation of absolute values, his demand for education which will be "useful" to the child, and his revolutionary thesis that schools must "condition behavior"—the very opposite of what schools in the West had heretofore considered their goal—all this offered a simple solution. Consequently, life adjustment has become the real objective of the American comprehensive school.

Life-adjustment teaching is not nearly so difficult as teaching algebra, French, or physics, and it is easier to learn, too. Life-adjustment training minimizes the vexing problem of mental inequalities since we are all equal when we buy groceries. So we have never really tried to find out what superior teaching might be able to do for average pupils. We have closed our eyes to what is done abroad by dismissing European education as undemocratic and unsuitable for this country. This shows an extraordinary lack of faith in the abilities of average American children. With strong motivation generated by home, school, and social influences, average middle- and upper-class children in Europe manage to get through their tough secondary schools. We have lacked the home and social influences because up to now success in life here did not depend on possession of a liberal-arts education. The schools have not cultivated respect for excellence, nor have they provided inspired teaching which might have brought average children into contact with the liberal arts and might well have kindled their interest. If our children have gone for the easy subjects, the fault has not been their own disinterest, laziness, or lack of ability; the fault has been poor adult guidance.

Henceforth, no one will be able to claim that a good liberal-arts education is aristocratic and not for the majority of our children. We are now faced with universal education of high caliber in Russia which "holds" Russian children to tough courses in free ten-year schools very like the European upper-track schools. Russian education proves one thing conclusively: properly motivated and deftly taught by competent teachers who know their subjects thoroughly, average children can reach far higher levels of education than even our talented children have achieved in most American public schools.[2] Failure to bring American pupils to levels of performance comparable to those of other advanced industrial countries is in large part a consequence of progressive educationist theories and practices.

Dewey has had a profound effect on American education. To many of our educators he is the *only* philosopher of education; there are no others. He has influenced both methods of teaching and content of curricula. The term "progressive education" usually calls forth a picture of teaching methods which permit the child to express himself freely. "The new spirit in education form the habit of requiring that every act be an outlet of the whole self," Dewey said. It is told that he once visited a classroom and found his own son helpless on the floor being beaten energetically by a bigger boy. "That is part of our progressive education," was the teacher's smug comment. We have no report on how Dewey reacted. Fortunately, progressive educational methods have not found too wide application in our schools—thanks primarily to the heroic resistance and good judgment of our teachers. However, the spirit of Dewey permeates our teachers' colleges and state boards of education; it thus influences the training

[2] See Chapter 9 and Appendix 3.

of our teachers and the formulation of school curricula. It makes its pernicious influence felt in the steady deterioration of secondary-school curricula, the prolongation of elementary schooling, and the denial to teachers of professional status.

In all fairness, we must give credit to Dewey and his followers for having improved what once was altogether too autocratic a relationship between teacher and pupil and for bringing a relaxed and friendly atmosphere into our classrooms. To this extent his influence on pedagogy has been beneficial. But his hatred of school discipline went too far and we see it contributing to the juvenile delinquency in this country, as well as to the failure of our schools to develop self-discipline in students—normally one of the basic objectives of formal education.

Two of Dewey's principles have profoundly influenced curricula. The first is his insistence that teaching must begin with subjects already known to the child and in which he expresses an interest. If this meant only that the child must be led from what is already known to him into the unknown, it would be a useful pedagogical device. In too many schools the child's experience becomes an end in itself and the learning process never gets off the ground. Illustrative is the statement of a high official of one of our state departments of education quoted by Professor Joel H. Hildebrand: "The elementary-school program, more than any other, has pioneered and paved the way to the creation of a truly child-centered, community-centered, life-centered, as opposed to subject-centered school."

The attitude of progressive educationists toward the curriculum is revealed in a pamphlet published by the Association for Supervision and Curriculum Development of the National Education Association, entitled *One Hundred Years of Curriculum Improvement, 1857–1957.* It first describes the deplorable situation existing in the benighted days before Dewey. In those days the curriculum "was organized according to the logic of a field, content was selected largely by experts in that field. Physicists wrote the text on physics; literature was selected and interpreted for high-school pupils by college professors; mathematicians decided on the order and content of arithmetic texts; and so *the experts dominated the content of the curriculum*." (My italics.) Fortunately, say the progressive educationists, such ridiculous ideas as that a physicist should determine the physics content of a high-school curriculum have long since been abandoned. Today, says the pamphlet, "experts in method and content" help "give breadth and vision" to curriculum revision. And furthermore, in accordance with "the philosophy of democratic participation and the recognition of the dynamic nature of learning," the pupils themselves will "set the goals, plan the activities, and evaluate the results of their work," gently led by teachers. The August 1958 *Bulletin* of the Council on Basic Education cheerfully comments: "If you want instruction in how to improve your tennis game, consult a plumber—or, better yet, do it yourself."

Dewey's insistence on making the child's interest the determining factor in planning curricula has led to substitution of know-how subjects for solid learning and to the widespread tendency of schools to instruct pupils in the minutiae of daily life—how to set a table correctly, how to budget one's income, how to use cameras, telephones, and consumer credit—the list is endless. Add to this that Dewey insisted the schoolroom must mirror the community and you find classrooms cluttered with cardboard boxes, children learning arithmetic by keeping store, and education stuck in the concrete and unable to carry the child from there to abstract concepts and ideas. Our young people are therefore deprived of the tremendous intellectual heritage of Western civilization which no child can possibly discover by himself; he must be led to it. We then get such grotesqueries as the following recommendation by a state education commission: As part of their work in history, it was suggested that high-school students should be asked to "make studies of how the last war affected the dating pattern of our culture."

The second item in Dewey's teaching is closely related to the first and has similarly watered down the scholastic content of curricula; the two reinforce each other. This second item is Dewey's insistence that each child should be taught only what will be "useful" to him. In a very broad sense, all education must be "useful" to the student; otherwise it would have no purpose. If Dewey's idea were interpreted as meaning that the child should be taught to make the best use of his mind, this would in truth be the most "useful" education one could give him. In practice, the test of "usefulness" has been interpreted in a narrower sense. The teaching of a foreign language, for example, has been considered useful only if it was actually spoken in the community. In the name of making schooling useful, many solid liberal-arts subjects have been eliminated. Their place has been taken by hundreds of vocational, recreational, personality, and etiquette courses, some actually compulsory. I know of a junior high school in a community where nearly all youngsters go to college and where, for some inexplicable reason, they must nevertheless take one semester course each in woodshop, print shop, and metal shop—each course teaches outdated and useless ways of handling woodwork, printing, or metalwork. One Midwest town recently inaugurated a compulsory eighth-grade course for boys and girls consisting of grooming, personality development, basic foods, wood finishing, painting, and electricity. As another example of this preoccupation with subjects not taught in school elsewhere, the model curriculum recently concocted by an assistant superintendent of schools includes "Science in Community Living," "Outdoor Science," "Landscape Gardening," "Consumer Chemistry," and to round this out nicely, "Atomic Power."

In their frantic search for something to interest the student or which may appear useful to him, our educationists reach the most extraordinary heights (or depths) of imagination. A recently published symposium on behavioral goals of high-school education in which seventy-five leading personages in American education collaborated contains a classification of desirable "behaviorial outcomes" for which high-school teaching should strive. In a review of this book the Council on Basic Education remarks that "the portrait of the Ideal High-school Graduate that emerges from this mass of stupefying detail is one of unexampled mediocrity. He is to do everything good and nothing well." Among his numerous and varied competencies are the following—this is merely a small sample: he "tries to draw logical conclusions"; he "helps when necessary to eliminate insects and vermin which tend to carry germs"; she (the girl graduate) "wears with growing self-assurance appropriate foundation garments and clothing properly styled for the maturing figure"; he "stands for and defends the right of each individual to worship God in his own way or refrain from religious affiliations and beliefs."

In a survey of education in his state, Dean Eston K. Feaster of West Virginia University last January gave us a glimpse of what this kind of schooling does to our children. West Virginia, though not among top-ranking states in public education, may nevertheless be taken as reflecting the general pattern accurately. The Feaster report brings out the tragic effect of present educationist policies on a child's interest in the things of the mind. "Regardless of the types of schools the pupils have come through," he writes, "however much interest in learning a very significant proportion (36 per cent) of them had in grades six and eight is completely, or almost completely, gone by the twelfth grade. . . . When more than three out of every four seniors in four large high schools call schooling exasperating and tedious, the situation is too serious to be laughed off."

In this book the emphasis is on high-school education, but we must not permit ourselves to think that all is well in the elementary schools. There is no doubt, unfortunately, that from the first grade on our children in public schools fall behind those in private schools here or in public schools abroad. When confronted with evidence that Europe's children complete their pre-professional education several years before our own, American educationists always brush this aside with the cliché that ours is mass, theirs is class, education. This is not a valid alibi for secondary-school education.

It is even less valid for elementary education since European children go to elementary school together for at least the first four years and often the first six. If they do better than our children in elementary school this must be either because (1) our teaching is inferior; or (2) our children are inferior. You can take your choice. I vote for the first.

For a comparison between achievements in a representative public and private school in this country, take the problems which are typical for the fourth grade in public school and the third grade in private school: The *nine-year*-old child in public school must solve this typical problem: "Peter's father is thirty-five years old. Peter is ten years old. How much older than Peter is his father?" Contrast this with the typical problem for an *eight-year*-old private-school pupil: "The dividend is $895.46. The divisor is 98; what is the quotient?"

Now for a comparison between public elementary schools here and in Switzerland. Professor Harold L. Clapp of the Language Department of Grinnell College—a long-time foe of life-adjustment education—describes the experiences of his children in public elementary school here and in Geneva. A Swiss fifth-grader will solve the following typical problem: "A stock of pamphlets is in three piles. The first pile contains one-sixth of them; the second pile contains several fifths of them; the third pile has four pamphlets. What is the total number of pamphlets?" A year later the American *sixth*-grader will have the following typical problem: "It took Tod one and two-thirds minutes to cut out a paper cat. At that rate, how many could be cut out in a half-hour. HELPER: First think, "a half-hour equals (?) minutes." Typical of our spoon-feeding pedagogy is this "Helper." Should a twelve-year-old American really need such assistance in solving this fantastically simple problem?

Both comparisons given are between public-school pupils who were a year ahead in grade of their little competitors but so very far behind in achievement. No wonder, then, that a comparison arithmetic test recently given representative eleven-year-olds in England and in central California showed the English children to have a two-to-one superiority in arithmetic achievement. This superiority of European school children as early as the elementary grades must be blamed wholly on our educationists. Despite the excessive emphasis given to pedagogy in teacher training here, techniques are obviously behind those in European schools where the teacher in addition is far better informed in his subject matter than his American colleague. Still, no public utterance of a good educationist is complete without his incantation that American schools are the "best in the world," the "envy of the world."

In the American comprehensive school the pupil finds a display of courses resembling the variegated dishes in a cafeteria—some useful to everyone (physical training), some useful to college-bound children (mathematics and sciences), some useful to future parents, homemakers, beauticians, printers, fishermen, and what have you. Out of this mass of subjects the child then chooses his fare. No wonder he often gorges himself on sweets instead of taking solid meat that must be chewed.

From leading educationists comes the alarming statement that "there is no aristocracy of 'subjects' . . . mathematics and mechanics, art and agriculture, history and homemaking are all peers." Thus, they tell us, it matters not what the child selects. One subject will do as much for his mind as any other. "Education," they say, "is guided living," its aims "are lines of growth not subject matter to be mastered." The curriculum must be based on "effective living now" and the "learner" is not out to absorb knowledge; he is "a goal-seeking organism reacting as an integrated whole to whole situations." For such goal-seeking boys, one school offers full courses on homemaking and etiquette, including use of silverware, "and how to order from a restaurant menu when on a date." Kilpatrick of Teachers College, principal disciple of Dewey, remarked that he "was not troubled . . . so long as the child is working fruitfully at some self-propelling social interest and . . . is interacting wholesomely in his social milieu."

Under progressive leadership, the American high school offers the majority of students a luxury-type elementary-school education, scholastically not much above the level of the lower-track European secondary continuation schools such as the English Modern School. In the midst of busy, happy, thoroughly unintellectual activities a minority of students pursue a sort of rudimentary college-preparatory course, inferior to that given in the upper-track European secondary schools. Despite the handicap of mixing serious studies with trivial pursuits, some American high schools succeed in maintaining respectable standards for which they deserve highest praise. But even there I venture to say that only a rare and occasional graduate could successfully pass the customary European secondary-school-leaving examination. More than a third of the Russian students who have access to the ten-year school (the plan is to have them everywhere in Russia by 1960) pass an examination at age seventeen which only a very few American high-school graduates could pass at eighteen.[3] Our high schools excel in turning out pleasant, attractive, friendly youngsters, but as *educational* institutions we cannot rate them high.

The pressure of masses of applicants now knocking at the college doors is about to have the same impact on the colleges that it previously had on the high schools. In fact, many colleges accommodated themselves some time ago to students who had practical or social rather than academic objectives. The great inflow which is about to begin will accelerate this trend. We already have colleges which are hardly better than secondary schools. We already have state universities which are required by law to admit all high-school graduates from the home state, or all those with a "C" average—obviously not college material. This shows up in the fantastic number of first-year failures—in some instances 40 per cent at the end of the freshman year. One might compare this with the 2 per cent first-year failures at Ivy League colleges where students have been carefully screened

[3] See Appendix 3.

for scholastic aptitude. Requiring state colleges to admit students who are unable to do college work is a waste of tax money which could be used to better advantage on higher salaries to obtain better teachers.

The American people have never authorized the schools to replace education with life-adjustment training and behavioral conditioning. Yet we have permitted the schools to experiment with Dewey's ideas for a long time. In all fairness, we can now—on his own pragmatic terms—declare the experiment to have failed and so reject Dewey's claim that experimentalist education fits the child for life in a technological society such as ours, and that it does this better than traditional education. There is a sort of Gresham's Law at work in American education. Levels are dropping all along the line. An average mark of 85 per cent today is equivalent to the bare average passing mark of 60 per cent a generation ago—indicative of the general downgrading of state requirements for the high-school diploma. Increasingly, the high schools must teach elementary subjects because the elementary schools have failed to do so. The colleges must give remedial courses in high school—sometimes even elementary school—subjects because freshmen cannot spell, write grammatically, express themselves or, as Dr. Killian remarked at a recent Senate hearing, because so many of them are mathematical illiterates. Each year we take pleasure in the greater number of American children going to school longer and reaching higher levels of education. But simultaneously the higher levels become lower so we end up where we began a hundred years ago—with an elementary-vocational education for the majority and a poor college-preparatory course for a minority of students; with some good colleges and many poor ones. The dream of American universal education has been betrayed.

We have not noticed this because we were constantly being told that ours was the best educational system in the world. Many parents were uneasy because they remembered having worked harder and advancing more rapidly in their own youth than their children in today's schools. They were

periodically soothed by tests allegedly proving that children
are better educated today than they were a generation ago.
No real basis of evaluation existed since few of us were familiar with schools in countries of similar levels of civilization. When it finally became evident that European children
were ahead of Americans, this was dismissed with the statement that ours is democratic education while Europe educates only its aristocracy. It may be helpful to interpolate a
brief résumé of European education at this point. It will
then be seen why customarily European secondary education separates the students with ability to absorb college-
preparatory programs from those who are unable to do so.
This is one of the main factors distinguishing their varied
schools from the single American omnibus school.

European education has a tradition that goes back to fifth-
century B.C. Athens. The Greeks, alone of all the nations of
the ancient world, placed knowledge and the power of
thought above all other pursuits as being most worthy of a
civilized man and a civilized state. We are indebted to them
for the marvelous pedagogical invention—the liberal-arts
curriculum—which has never been surpassed for training the
young to think, to use their brains in solving particular problems, and to provide them with general knowledge on which
specialized training could later safely be superimposed. We
are rediscovering the fact that a professional man needs the
foundation of a liberal-arts education in order to use his
specialized training wisely. The man who is highly trained
in only one field of knowledge and illiterate in all others can
be a positive danger to society.

Rome went to school in Greece, and so Greek ideas spread
through the Roman Empire. When the western half of the
empire collapsed under the onslaught of Germanic barbarians, a civilization disappeared from western Europe in
which there were more literate people, more books, more
libraries, and more schools than at any other time during the
next thousand years. Not until the classics were rediscovered
did Europe emerge from the Dark Ages. Only a glimmer of
ancient learning was kept alive in the West by the Church.

But Graeco-Roman civilization lived on in the eastern half of the Roman Empire to the end of the Middle Ages. More Greek than Roman, the Byzantine Empire waxed and waned in power, constantly beset by warlike barbarians who outnumbered the beleaguered citizens but could not conquer them, largely because the Byzantines were intellectually far superior to their neighbors. Greek ideas were taught in their schools and many proved extremely practical for defense. The Byzantines had one of the first "terror weapons"—the famous Greek fire—which won them many battles. Roman law and organization made the small state stronger than its scattered disorganized enemies. But gradually the empire shrank. Large chunks of land—the whole, highly civilized Near East passed to Islam with many flourishing universities. These the Arabs supported and in them classical learning was preserved. The Crusades brought the brave but uncouth knights of the West into contact with the civilized East, and so some classical knowledge was carried back by them to western Europe. This started a revival of learning and also the appearance of the first real universities; there were 108 by 1600.

A second influx of classical learning followed the fall of Byzantium to the Turks in 1453. The survival of this outpost of classical civilization for a millennium after the fall of Rome was a miracle. It can only be explained as a victory of mind over matter; of the superiority of people of Graeco-Roman civilization over less civilized peoples. The city was taken in the end by treachery. But even in defeat the Byzantines passed on the torch of civilization. Refugees carried precious Greek and Roman writings to the West where these helped to bring about that sudden and magnificent explosion of intellectual and artistic creativity which we call the Renaissance. Greek medical science was rediscovered and led to establishment of medical faculties in all Western universities. Greek concepts of the rights and duties of professional men spread and influenced the establishment of Europe's excellent system of professional training in universities. When the famed Fibonacci introduced Arabic numerals, mathematics advanced rapidly. Greek philosophy stimulated the West to scientific thinking and thereby gave impetus to the scientific discoveries which carried Europe rapidly to the height of political, economic, and intellectual eminence. Without formal education—without universities and university-preparatory schools—none of this could have happened.

Since Latin was the language of the Church and churchmen made up the faculties of medieval and early Renaissance universities, Latin was the language which everyone had to learn who wished to enter a university and study for a professional career. Greek was also widely used. To prepare youngsters for entrance into the universities, "Latin schools" were founded. These schools gave a classical education preparatory to enrollment in the university. Sometimes these schools were attached to a cathedral, sometimes they were set up by private endowment, or founded by kings as charitable institutions for children of poor or deceased courtiers. Latin or grammar schools, as they are still called in England, are the forerunners of European—and of early American—secondary schools.

Together with this education for children destined for political leadership or for professional careers there developed an entirely separate system of education for the common people. In the late Middle Ages, cities rose to power and wealth. Their craftsmen and merchants found that elementary knowledge—the three "R's"—was of practical use to them. Since their children did not intend to enter the universities, Latin was not needed, and teaching was in the vernacular. These schools were the forerunners of the elementary schools later taken over by the state. As countries advanced technologically, the minimum amount of education needed by every citizen increased. Elementary education originally lasted for three years but was gradually extended to eight. Gradually vocational continuation schools were added to the eight-year elementary school. Child labor laws freed children from early labor and made compulsory education feasible. The school leaving age in much of Europe is fifteen to sixteen; in the United States it is in general sixteen.[4] Free and compulsory elementary education was introduced in some European countries long before we ourselves took that step. Most continental European governments took over all or a major share of educational costs —from kindergarten to university—during the eighteenth and nineteenth centuries. School fees were modest on the Continent. In England, however, education for the upper classes was private and expensive; education for the rest of the people was not so good as that on the Continent until the late nineteenth century. English public education is now first-rate and open to all children who can qualify by passing examinations at age eleven.

Although since World War I European education has been made available to larger and larger numbers of children and inability to pay school fees no longer bars the gifted child from the highest education, the separate academic and nonacademic tracks have been retained.

At ten or eleven, if they can pass the entrance examinations for academic secondary schools, children may enter the upper track—about 15 to 20 per cent achieve this. The remainder enter one of several other types of secondary schools, depending on whether they seek a general education not so demanding as that of the academic secondary schools, or whether they seek immediate training for their future careers. In the latter case they enter a commercial or trade school which gives some general education but with emphasis on vocational training.

The upper-track secondary schools carry the student up to eighteen or nineteen, at which age he is considered to have received sufficient liberal-arts or general education to permit him to begin study for a professional career at institutions of university rank. Most of the liberal-arts education given in our colleges has been absorbed into the curricula of the European academic secondary schools; the remainder

[4] Leaving age in 39 states, sixteen; 4 states, seventeen; 5 states, eighteen.

has been incorporated into the faculties of philosophy of the universities.

The European student is ready for professional study two to three years sooner than his American counterpart because he has been placed at an early age in the upper-track secondary school which he attends for from six to nine years. Because he stays so long in one school in which the level of intelligence is fairly homogeneous, the schools can plan his course of study carefully, subject following subject in logical sequence. There are no electives but there is a choice of three different kinds of upper-track secondary schools—classical; modern, with emphasis on the sciences; and a third type which combines parts of both.

Most European countries put almost as large a percentage of their much smaller national income into educating their children as we do. Since their populations grow very slowly they do not need so much for new capital investment in education, but they do have to make their money go as far as possible. Thus they do not waste it on frills or on keeping children above sixteen in school after they manifestly cannot absorb any more learning. Their schooling is tailored to fit the aptitudes of children as determined by examination. Teachers are on the lookout for gifted pupils and urge parents to let them go to schools preparing for the university. The careful manner in which European school authorities find the proper type of schooling for each child's individual gifts is often criticized here as cruel and undemocratic. Weeding out by means of examinations, in particular, arouses pity and horror. Most Americans seem to regard education as a sort of commodity or service which anybody ought to be permitted to "get" simply by paying tuition or by having the cost of education met through taxes. We have yet to learn that education is one thing that money alone cannot purchase. *The only acceptable coin which buys an education is hard intellectual effort.* How much education can be bought with mental effort depends on the quality of the teacher and of the pupil. Strong motivation can often offset a modest I.Q., and we also know that a high I.Q. without strong motivation can be ineffective. All that a democratic government can do to insure educational equality for all its children is to throw open the school to everyone who will make the effort to learn. This most of our European friends have long been doing. Insistence on intellectual effort is where we have fallen down.

European children go to school six days a week, their school day is longer, and school vacations are shorter than here. Frequent examinations weed out the incompetent or the lazy. But Europe's most important educational achievement is that despite pressures, not unlike those exerted on the schools here, she has democratized the educational process by reducing or abolishing school fees but has refused to be stampeded into lowering the quality of secondary and university education; this remains, as it has for a hundred and fifty years, the best in the world.

European schools are neither social clubs nor finishing schools. Their objectives are limited and clearly defined: they seek to equip the child with all the intellectual tools he can handle; they nourish his mind with as much general culture as he can absorb; and they give his body all the exercise it can take. When a point is reached where pupils can absorb no more mental food, they go on to schools which give vocational training of one kind or another.

In contrast to the businesslike manner in which European schools conduct their pupils through their respective study programs, a pernicious mañana spirit permeates our public elementary and secondary schools. The time when pupils come to grips with real study has for years been progressively delayed. Each year the American child drops a bit further behind his contemporaries abroad. He still cannot spell in his own language at an age when children abroad are already deep in serious literature and are carrying one or more foreign languages, besides heavier schedules in mathematics, sciences, history, and so on. Recently I was told of a German exchange student who, though an average student at home, not only found school here ridiculously easy, but actually stood highest in English—mind you in English!—among his American high-school classmates.

The excuse for this procrastination is always that our education is democratic and that of Europe aristocratic. This is an erroneous and spurious alibi. Except for relatively short periods of time, European higher education, even in the past, has been primarily the concern of the middle class, with scholarships available for talented children of the poor. In fact, education has been the principal channel of social advancement for gifted children of Europe's lower middle class —artisans, farmers, clerks. The aristocratic father did not find it necessary to subject his son to the rigorous mental discipline of higher learning until his privileges had begun to decline and he had to compete with the rising middle class.

Not school fees, but inability to finance years of unproductive life for their children, has kept the European masses from higher education. Europe is simply poorer than we for lack of ample land and natural resources. Also, in class societies parents tend to feel that what was good enough for them is good enough for their children. The desire to give our children a better education than we have had ourselves goes hand in hand with a high standard of living and an expansive optimism such as has prevailed in our country since its beginning.

But in Europe also the level of life has risen and democracy has been growing steadily. There, too, proportionately more children now attend academic secondary schools and universities. For example, between 1850 and 1950 the population of the Netherlands tripled but the number of university students multiplied twenty-eight times.

The excellence of the European educational systems is demonstrated by the large number of Europeans who have distinguished themselves in all spheres of the human spirit. Take the Nobel prize winners, for example:

Through 1955 the Nobel Prize Committee in awarding prizes for original work in physics and chemistry granted, in proportion to population, three times as many to Germany as to the United States; two and one half times as many to

England; one and one half times as many to France. Most astonishing, perhaps, Holland with a population one sixteenth of ours received four to our twenty-two prizes; Switzerland, with one thirty-fifth, received five prizes; Austria, with one twenty-third, got three. Take the field of nuclear fission alone: twelve basic discoveries in physics, chemistry, and mathematics brought atomic power into being. Of these, three each were made by German, English, and French scientists; one each by Danish and Italian scientists; and only one by an American. Yet the population of Germany, England, France, Denmark, and Italy combined is only one third greater than that of the United States; their total national wealth is far less than ours. In this particular field of trained brain power they were eleven times as rich as we.

Or, again, take the successful development of the atomic bomb: we provided excellent direction, extensive facilities, unlimited funds, but the major contributions in brain power came from such men as Italy's Fermi and Segré; Denmark's Bohr; Hungary's Teller, Von Neumann, Wigner and Szilard; Germany's Hahn, Strassman, Bethe, and Einstein; England's Chadwick and Cockcroft—to mention but a few of the top men. In fact, it was of no small concern to the Joint Congressional Committee on Atomic Energy that the very topmost of our scientists are 60 to 70 per cent foreign-born and educated. Even some of our native-born top scientific contributors received their university training abroad.

These are examples familiar to me as an engineer. They could be duplicated in many other fields.

Dewey's influence on American educators has been deep and lasting. His claim that "the primary business of the school is to train children in cooperative and mutually helpful living" is, I submit, an erroneous conception of education in a dynamic, competitive society such as ours. We have abandoned excellence in order to keep every child in school till almost adulthood, regardless of whether he profits from school learning or not. Neither the leaders of American education nor this country's parents have been able to face up to the inequality of native endowment in our children, and so we have not been able to work out clear-cut, logical study programs for them. We have been so obsessed with "democracy" and "equality" that smart and industrious children have been denied praise and dull and lazy ones have escaped censure in the name of "democracy in the classroom." There was a time in our history when children were flunked when they failed their exams and were given "D's" for poor homework. We were no less democratic then than we are today; we were merely more sensible.

Piecemeal attempts to toughen the schools will not, I fear, effect the necessary reforms that would put our educational system in the forefront—at least ahead of the Russians. We must first be clear in our minds as to what we want our schools to accomplish. What sort of persons would we like the young graduates to be? What kind of education would be of greatest use to them as human beings, as citizens, and as breadwinners?

Each of us must find his own answer to this question, and must then express his wishes clearly and in a proper democratic way to those who run our schools. For what it may be worth, here is my own answer:

Formal education in schools should, I believe, be clearly differentiated from such learning as may be termed "incidental"—what the child picks up in the home, in association with contemporaries and adults, and from his personal experiences. *The school's concern is with the intellect alone.* Young people in this modern world need minds that are well stocked with the kind of knowledge that makes life intelligible. No substitute for a liberal-arts education has yet been invented that serves this purpose so well. English, foreign languages, mathematics, sciences, history, geography—these are the subjects which must be mastered. They are the intellectual tools that enable us to order our lives intelligently —to understand the complexities of today's tense and uncertain world. Those who do not have the mentality to master all these subjects need the same *kind* of intellectual fare, only less of it.

A school succeeds when it sends its graduates into the world with minds which function markedly better because of time spent in the classroom. The child's own endowments and his determination to develop them will of course set limits as to what the schools can do for him. All we have a right to expect of the schools is that they will strengthen his determination and allow no other limits but those set by nature to impede any child's intellectual progress.

Unfortunately, the wrong kind of school handicaps the child's progress. Children are barred from mental growth where high tuition withholds education from poor children; just as much harm is done when pupils are forced into an intellectual strait jacket for the sake of democratic equalitarianism. A school system which insists on the same instruction for the talented, the average, and the below-average child prevents as many children from growing intellectually as does a system that excludes children because of the social, political, or economic status of their parents. Neither system is democratic. Attendance figures may be impressive but they mean little when they represent attendance in schools where the mind lies fallow.

Nothing we bestow upon our children in the way of material advantages can compare with the gift of a good education. We often speak of democratic freedom, and of course we treasure it. Basic to political freedom is personal independence; and this can exist only when the mind has been unshackled from ignorance, from dependence on the opinions of others, and from fear of disagreeable facts. Bombarded as all of us are, all day long, by subtle sloganeers seeking to convert us to their views, we sorely need minds that have been sharpened by hard intellectual work. We must know how to dig up our own facts—how to discover truth for ourselves. The person who has learned to trust only proven facts, who knows how to find and recognize truth, and who has been trained to decide all issues on the basis of truth and reason—he and he alone is a free man.

In my opinion, the purpose of schools is to help children to develop minds which are free, because no inner deficiencies or outer pressures can then bar them from truth and, through truth, from inner freedom. I believe with Francis Bacon that "It is heaven upon earth, to have a man's mind ... turn upon the poles of truth," and this I want for all our children.

Chapter 9

THE BALANCE SHEET ON
EDUCATION

The powerful thrust of Sputnik's launching device did more than penetrate outer space. It also pierced the thick armor encasing our complacent faith in America's present and future technological supremacy. It blasted the comfortable conviction that only in an atmosphere of personal independence and political liberty can science and scientists flourish. It shook the belief, long taken for granted, that a high standard of material well-being is both the outward manifestation and the necessary basis for technological progress.

It did greatest damage to our trust in the American educational system—up to now almost as sacrosanct as motherhood. Harsh words are being said about its methods no less than about its aims. Sputnik has been seen as a triumph of Russian education, and rightly so. Reams of words and figures have filled the newspaper columns describing Russian education, comparing it with ours, and trying to pin point where we have failed in the vital educational task of motivating and training the skilled professionals needed by our country while Russia seems to have no trouble turning them out in vast numbers.

We are asking searching questions about the aims of education in a modern technological society and how our schools can best achieve them. We are finally coming out of our traditional educational isolation and looking at the educational systems of other countries of Western civilization in order to compare them with ours. But we are still not ready to do this in a spirit of detachment, as I shall show later. The whole reappraisal has been painful but good for us.

157

Sputnik may well be the catalyst which brings about drastic and long-overdue reforms in utilizing the nation's intellectual resources. It may thus do in matters of the intellect what Pearl Harbor did in matters industrial and military. Then, as now, a dramatic occurrence suddenly revealed that we had failed to develop our capacities to their maximum potential. As we found then that in a national emergency we could take prompt and vigorous action and perform industrial miracles, so I am convinced we can now take similar action and perform educational miracles.

Let us not lose our heads and despair of American technological competence *as it is today.* The real danger lies somewhat in the future and can be averted if we will act. At the moment, I for one am convinced that we have the men and the resources which, if properly directed and given priority, could have put a satellite in orbit ahead of the Russians. This, of course, is no excuse for our mistake in letting Russia win a propaganda victory, damaging to our prestige among the uncommitted nations of the world and, it is to be feared, also among some of our friends.

The Sputnik was aloft first, and that is regrettable. What is particularly regrettable is that to many people it looks not like a military weapon but like pure, scientific adventure of a kind which appeals to their imagination as no superior weapon could. Russia indeed chose shrewdly where to concentrate for a blow to our scientific and technological prestige. It also fits nicely into the International Geophysical Year. In actual fact, Sputnik is of course of great military significance because of its relation to missile weaponry and because of the potential military advantages of outer-space control.

The successful Russian satellite program brings out two important facts which we would disregard at our peril: *First,* it demonstrates conclusively that a modern totalitarian state can depress the standard of living of its people to the level of the most backward of countries while simultaneously raising a limited sector of the economy to a standard as high as, if not higher than, comparable sectors of the economy of the most highly developed country in the world. Theoretically, the favored sector could be any one chosen as of greatest national importance by the rulers of a totalitarian state; in practice it will inevitably be the sector which significantly benefits the country's military and political power. *Second,* it proves that a modern despotism can devise an educational system shaped solely in the interest of the state and in complete disregard of the needs of the individual child, and yet induce *all* children to stretch their intellectual capacities to the utmost. These factors are worth examining in more detail.

We are of course familiar with the total power exercised by the self-chosen rulers of modern totalitarian states. We have known that they could and did manipulate the productive capacity of their countries in a way which puts heavy industry and armaments production ahead of production of consumer goods. But most of us felt that in the long run they would be forced to strike a better balance. I believe we must now accept as fact a permanent imbalance, probably of increasing proportion, between the civilian and the politico-military sector of the Russian economy. The very backwardness of the civilian sector, far from hampering progress, is proving an advantage to Russia's rulers.

Unrest in Soviet-dominated countries, where communism is a foreign importation, which brought with it a steep decline in the economic well-being of the people and deterioration in their spiritual life, does not mean that similar unrest will necessarily appear in Russia herself. What must not be forgotten is that almost everyone who had enjoyed material well-being under the old Russian regime was killed or driven out. The rest of the people have never known greater material benefits or more political freedom than they are now permitted to enjoy. If anything, they live better. Though they do not have so much milk or meat as in pre-revolutionary days, they now have something which gives greater satisfaction to a people from whom the world of books, of ideas, of music, and art had for centuries been withheld. They have a chance at an education, limited and utilitarian as it may be; they have greater opportunities to see a show, a ballet, to hear concert music, even if they must queue up for hours to obtain tickets. Measured against the past, the Russian standard of living is not in itself low enough to cause unrest, and comparison with life in other countries is carefully prevented.

Authoritarian control and the low standard of living make the running of the civilian sector simple and cheap. It takes less time, effort, and money to issue orders and deaden independent thought by propaganda than to seek consent by marshaling convincing arguments and winning free-and-open discussions. The cost in time and money of the whole paraphernalia of parliamentary or congressional government is eliminated. Cost of mass media can be kept at a fraction of what is customary in free countries, and the personnel required need be neither so numerous nor so competent.

The entire business complex is missing and in its place there is a weak consumer-industries sector which merely has to keep people reasonably warm, adequately fed, and provided with a roof over their heads. There is no need for attractive stores, for service industries, for advertising. Almost the whole automobile complex is lacking. No chain of garages, auto dealers, service stations, etc. All that are needed are trucks and a few cars for the elite. One could go on *ad infinitum*.

Obviously, given similar resources in land and population, the modern totalitarian state can put into the politico-military sector many times as much wealth and man power as a democratic country. With the same number of scientists and engineers concentrating on a few projects deemed of great national importance, spectacular technological breakthroughs can be achieved. Moreover, the meager demands of the civilian economy on irreplaceable mineral and fuel resources prevent rapid deterioration of the country's resources base such as now threatens all highly developed countries. When all the gasoline has been burned up by the American family car, Russia may still have a reserve in the ground for her planes, submarines, and tanks.

All non-totalitarian countries are multiple-purpose societies in which national income as well as national wealth and
man power is allocated to different sectors of the economy
under the price system of the open market. Even where
democracy is but a feeble force, governments are in practice
not free to dispose arbitrarily of people and property except
in time of war. In our country, as in all countries of Western
civilization, it is the value judgments of the average man
which determine how the country's man power and productive capacity are to be utilized. I believe that everywhere
the average man makes decisions by judging how they
would affect, first, himself and his family; second, the group
with which he is most closely associated—neighborhood,
political party, religious, professional, or ethnical group;
and last the nation as a whole. For some few there is a fourth
category—the world.

This order of values is often self-defeating. A man may
feel that his personal interest in tax reduction outweighs
the importance of good public education; or he may feel
that the money his firm can save by letting industrial wastes
pollute a river outweighs the interest of the community in
preserving aesthetic values, natural beauty, and a pure
water supply; or that he has the right to use pressure tactics
to increase his income even if this will result in inflation. He
may feel that he has a better right to the biggest, heaviest
automobile than the nation has to conserve a dwindling
stock of irreplaceable minerals and fuels; he would like the
country's foreign policy to favor his parents' country of origin whether this is to the advantage of our country as a
whole or not. Re-examination of such judgments will often
show that they have actually done more harm to the narrower interests than would have a decision which puts wider
interests first.

In our country the major share of all our technical effort
has gone into spreading ever higher standards of material
well-being over ever larger segments of the population.
Perhaps too large an effort has gone into the things that
make American life pleasant and comfortable and not

enough into the things that insure continuous spiritual and
material growth as well as military and political victory in
any war, hot or cold.

In the long run, the more disturbing fact which is dis-
closed by the Russian satellite program is Russia's success
in building in record time an educational system which
produces exactly the sort of trained men and women her
rulers need to achieve technological supremacy the day
after tomorrow. Russian education is, of course, deplorably
utilitarian and authoritarian. However, it has virtually wiped
out illiteracy; today estimated to be only 2.5 to 5 per cent,
which does not compare badly with our own rate—3.7 per
cent in 1940 and about 2.5 per cent today. Russia has put a
larger percentage of her *smaller* national income into public
education than the United States. She has made the rewards
of intellectual accomplishment so attractive that her children are working extremely hard to keep up with a tough
curriculum. Russia has as great a shortage as we in school
buildings—she merely doubles up and so gets twice the
benefit we do out of each classroom and school laboratory.
I feel sure she would use her schools on a three-shift basis if
this were necessary. Russia has no teacher shortage, no sub-
standard teachers—she has set their scholastic standards
high and gives them a heavy work load, but she also honors
them and pays them well. Russia evidently has no difficulty
getting intelligent people with solid education in their
chosen subjects to work devotedly and without worrying
too much about lack of political freedom. This has been a
surprise to us—an unpleasant surprise.

Had we looked at the matter from the point of view of
the peasant children earnestly studying in classroom, laboratory, and library we would not have been so surprised. The
low standard of living and the memory of a past, meager in
culture, are assets to the Soviets. It is difficult for us to
understand the intense longing for education—any kind of
education—of underdeveloped people. This is a strong bond
that unites Russia—no longer underdeveloped but close

enough to the immediate backward past—with all the underdeveloped people of the world.

Moreover, it is far easier to awaken in children a sense of personal achievement, of victory, in mastering the intellectual challenge of tough curricula, if there are no competing attractions such as those which claim the attention of our more fortunate children: no comfortable home, playrooms, and back yards to play in; no juke boxes; far fewer movies; hardly any distracting radio or TV programs; no senior proms, dating, long telephone conversations, and of course no hot rods. If they could have them, these pleasant things would greatly delight Russia's youngsters and probably cut into their study time; witness their avid interest in American jive and rock-'n-roll records—to the dismay of the authorities. Russia does have a problem with unruly so-called young hooligans who are—and this is significant—not the children of the poor, but the pampered offspring of Russia's elite. Eventually there may be more of these disturbing youths, but for the moment they hardly make a dent in the picture of an earnest, well-disciplined, polite, and studious school population.

It has surprised us to find that Russia's intellectual elite does highly competent work despite authoritarian control in all—even the highest—educational and research institutions. Russia appears to have found a way of allowing superior minds freedom in the field of their special competence while denying them the right of political criticism. It has apparently been possible to develop the critical capacity of superior minds to the high degree needed for scientific work while fettering it in all other fields. There is evidence that the fetters are well hidden, and that discontent with Russian life is largely prevented. This seems to be done by shrewdly catering to the needs of these people both as scientists and as ordinary men and women. They are allowed to let their minds roam undisturbed in quest of knowledge; they are given superb laboratory and research facilities; the best thoughts of foreign scientists are gathered quickly from scientific magazines and books the world over and presented by large staffs of abstracters to any Russian scientist who needs them; honors are heaped on scientists and engineers for superior achievements although they do not so often get their names in the papers as do their colleagues in the free world, for this would smack of "personality cult."

Scientists also have needs of the kind common to all mortals, so Russia gives them attractive living quarters, country houses, vacations, maids, cars, and chauffeurs. Their pay is in the top-income bracket; in fact, the highest salary in Russia is paid to the president of the Soviet Academy of Sciences. Why should these men concern themselves about the lack of political freedom or the grim and dreary life of most of their compatriots? They probably reason that these are temporary abuses and that their own scientific work will contribute to the wealth and power of their country and thus ultimately to a better life for everyone. Quite possibly, too, totalitarian states may have a built-in incentive for attracting gifted minds to science: the desire to escape from the grim reality of life to a safe and comfortable ivory tower.

It is an unfortunate accident of history for us that today the military and political power of a country depends so largely on having a highly developed technical civilization. This, in turn, calls for vast numbers of scientists and engineers. The subjects which these men must master are mathematics, physics, chemistry, astronomy—all apparently regarded as politically safe by Russia's rulers. Even the most fanatic Marxist would have trouble interjecting the party line into these particular sciences. It is different, however, with other sciences. Take biology: this is a science which heretofore could not be freely pursued in Russia. Scientific truth had to be sacrificed to the Lysenko-Stalin theory of genetics. Other than party-line limitations may also restrict free scientific inquiry. For example, Russia does not presently consider it necessary to excel in medical research. Chemists are therefore diverted from inquiries which might cure diseases of man to inquiries which can improve metals. The results of costly foreign medical research are instantly available to Russia so she can shift appropriations from the medical to the engineering faculty and save money and man power.

Enough has been said to give an inkling of the methods by which the Soviet manipulates its skilled man power. It might be noted in passing that the fields in which they have done outstanding work have been precisely those where they were allowed maximum intellectual freedom. Little that is new and original has come out of Russia in other fields, but second-rate theater, literature, art, etc., are not of great importance in today's international power relationships.

Faced with this formidable and ruthless adversary who has openly promised "to bury" us and who grows daily in industrial and military might, what are we to do?

First, I think, we must awaken America to the danger facing the nation—making public all the facts without soothing the impact of unpleasant truths. I have no doubt that as a people we have enough patriotism, let alone enlightened self-interest, to recognize that we must put greater effort into the things which will make America strong, even if this may require a reappraisal of cherished convictions and ways of life; even at the cost of some material sacrifices, which I doubt would be large.

Ours is an enormously productive economy, the first in history which produces a large surplus over and above reasonable necessities of life. The flood of goods coming off our production lines is so tremendous that some ten billion dollars must be spent annually to encourage disposal of them. I speak, of course, of advertising, which costs us as much as all of our primary and secondary public schools put together. This is money with which advertisers finance our mass media and through them ceaselessly hammer at the need for ever more and better goods and services. People must be made to buy things for which they feel no need; they must be induced to replace possessions still entirely satisfactory for new ones which, it is promised, will make them up to date and enhance their family's prestige. The subconscious is probed in order to find ways in which to stifle the still voice of conscience and induce the American people to go into consumer debts of more than three billion dollars annually—42 billion standing on the books as of now. Often young children are conditioned to act as unpaid boosters for higher consumption.

Last year it cost the automobile industry alone 1½ billion dollars to design and bring out new models. This appears to be the only way to insure that American families will continue to spend 10 per cent of their income on cars. One and a half billion dollars is three fourths of what the nation paid for education in all its public colleges and universities. I mention these figures to show that sacrifices to give America strength in the race with Russia would be insignificant in view of our enormous margin of luxury spending.

Second, and equally important, I believe, we must reverse our treatment of scientists and trained professionals. It is easy to make a good living in this country without much serious education. Hence the temptation to do this is so great that it can be offset only by deliberate actions to elevate the status of professional people in terms both of prestige and of material reward. We had better stop calling scientists "long hairs" or "little men with beards." In the present mood of chastisement, scientists have been speaking up and telling us that such disparaging remarks hurt and may have discouraged many a young man from choosing the hard intellectual road to science rather than the easy and pleasant road to business success and country-club living.

Merely spending a lot of money on scientists, scientific research, and new military projects will not be enough. In final analysis trained man power can only come out of a thoroughly reorganized educational system with totally different aims and considerably higher scholastic standards. To carry through such drastic reforms is a formidable undertaking, but reforms of similar magnitude have been carried out elsewhere in the past.

Much could be learned from Europe's educational experience in particular, for Europe is old and wise at educating the young. Some of her famous universities have been in the business for a longer time than the white man has been in North America. Formal education itself is a European invention and probably the main factor in her phenomenal success, first in colonizing the world and then, so to speak, setting it on its feet with the mark of European civilization so deeply imbedded that it may well prove ineradicable. Nowhere else has there been a spontaneous, native growth; wherever formal education exists today it was brought by European settlers or colonial administrators.

One thing we in this country might learn from Europe is how to keep education in step with changing times. This sometimes necessitates a reform of such magnitude as to resemble a revolution in education. There have been two such upheavals in Russia: in 1917 and in the early 1930's. The first abolished the Czarist school system and established a new type of workers' education, influenced to some degree by the philosophical theories of John Dewey and by American progressive experiments; the second abolished this system and returned to a Marxist version of the continental European system.

There have been other less drastic school reforms elsewhere. In fact the entire nineteenth century was one of constant change toward better and more widespread education in the entire Western world and, influenced by the West, in many underdeveloped countries as well. England changed her education drastically over a period of almost a hundred years, from the mid-1800's until the post-World War II reform period. Once the most aristocratic and expensive education in the world, limited to a small segment of the upper middle class and the aristocracy, English public education is now first-rate in quality and entirely open to all who can qualify. Two other major educational reforms are of interest. One, the reorganization of Prussian education after the country's defeat by Napoleon in 1806; the other France's reorganization of the elementary-school system after her defeat by Prussia in 1871.

No educational reform is ever easy. It is more quickly put

through where governments need not consult their people. This gives authoritarian countries such as Prussia an advantage over democratic countries such as England in the matter of keeping education in step with changing conditions. Similarly, it is giving totalitarian Russia an advantage over us which will take great effort on our part to overcome.

Because of her ability to reform her schools rapidly and to fit her educational system to the needs of the nineteenth century, Prussia eventually closed the wide gap in economic and political power, wealth, and scientific achievement which had separated her from England at the time of the Napoleonic Wars. England's difficulties with educational reform are instructive for us because there was a conflict between church and state for control over schools comparable to our federal versus local control issue. In England a wise compromise was finally worked out whereby in return for acceptance of certain national standards the local schools were given state aid. The Russian reforms are interesting because Russia's recent forging ahead in science and technology followed upon her abandonment of damaging educational theories akin to those of the progressive educationists who have hurt our own schools as well. One can always learn from the experience of others. I shall briefly describe the Prussian reform of 1806 which was of the greatest significance since it set a pattern for secondary and higher education followed in many other European states. I shall also give an account of Russia's two major educational upheavals.

After her crushing defeat by Napoleon, Prussia put through a series of reforms in her political, social, and educational institutions in order to achieve enough strength to strike a blow for liberty. In 1806 the country lay prostrate under the heel of the conqueror, her richest lands torn away, her treasury empty. Poor though she was, Prussia had to bring the entire country rapidly from the seventeenth to the nineteenth century or forego all hope of ever rising again. A small band of devoted men did the country over from top to bottom, including the school system, which had deteriorated because of inadequate financial support and poorly trained teachers. The famed statesman Von Humboldt was put in charge of reforming education.

Prussia was one of the first countries to recognize that a modern state must have a citizenry with at least an elementary education; that it must have leaders sufficiently educated to deal with the problems of the coming industrial and scientific age. She was one of the first to make elementary education compulsory and free and to put all education under state control. Being a poor country, she could not afford to educate her future leaders in the leisurely and costly manner in which this was done in wealthy England through the "public-school" system and the residential universities of Oxford and Cambridge. Prussia actually had similar residential preparatory schools which she might have used as the nucleus of a new educational system; these were boarding schools for the nobility. But when she set up public secondary education she realistically cut out all features not necessary for education *per se*. Because the people were poor, fees had to be kept low; so a large part of the cost of education had to be borne by the state. Hence the carefully thought-out businesslike way in which she worked out her two-track system: one track designed for the mass of children, the other for those destined for the higher professions.

The rapid rise of Prussia to industrial and military power and the excellence of the scientific research done at her universities—to which students soon flocked from all over the world—led to widespread adoption of her basic educational system by most of continental Europe. Her lightning victories in 1864, 1866, and 1871—a mere half century after she had been soundly beaten by France—were recognized everywhere as a victory of the Prussian schools and universities. To defeated France the lesson was plain; she took energetic measures to modernize her own educational system.

The Humboldt reforms concentrated on two aspects of education: the training and status of teachers and the content of the traditional secondary-school-leaving certificate required of all who wished to enroll in a university. The state set standards for both. Teachers were raised to the status of professionals and in return a very thorough knowledge of subject matter was required of them before they received certification from the state. Teacher training and salary were graded according to the amount of subject knowledge required: it was lowest for the elementary schoolteacher, higher for the secondary-school professor whose education involved several years of university study, and highest for the university professor who achieved this position only after a very long period of study and research, as well as after giving clear evidence of scholastic attainments of the highest order.

The secondary-school-leaving certificate—the *Abitur* (comparable to the French *baccalauréat*)—was likewise made uniform throughout Prussia, and subsequently throughout Germany. It was a diploma granted after a prolonged period of oral and written examinations supervised by authorities not connected with the school whose pupils were being tested. The questions and problems in these tough examinations were worked out carefully by the scholarly members of the Prussian Ministry of Education and were designed to cover the entire range of knowledge encompassed in the secondary school program. In Prussia, and later in Germany, the Abitur comes at the end of nine years of secondary education, in Austria of eight, in France of seven, and in Holland of six years. The differences in length have little to do with the end result. They merely indicate the age when the upper-track pupils are separated from the lower-track pupils. In all advanced European countries the secondary-school-leaving certificates are of comparable value and entitle students to enter the universities of any European country at age eighteen to nineteen. England alone has an educational system which stands aloof from those of the continental countries.

Europe's universities are anchored in a common past going back to Greece, Rome, and the medieval unity of Church and empire. It had always been the custom for European students to go wherever they could find the best professor in their special field of interest, even when this meant crossing national boundaries. A semester taken abroad counted as much toward the winning of a degree as one taken at home. To preserve this valuable educational mobility the several countries of necessity had to maintain uniformly high standards for the traditional secondary-school-leaving certificate. A country that allowed this certificate to fall below standard would lose prestige and bar study at foreign universities to its students. At first all secondary schools gave a classical education. When Latin ceased to be the language of educated men and it was found that modern industrial nations needed fewer classical scholars and more people whose schooling stressed mathematics, science, and modern languages, new secondary schools were established. These were either semi-classical or mathematics-science schools.

Though different subjects are taught in these three basic kinds of secondary schools the quality of the instruction is identical, as is the rigor of the final examination. All school-leaving certificates are therefore qualitatively the same, though they represent different kinds of knowledge.

A century later than the rest of Europe Russia was in a similar predicament; her schools, too, were unable to educate children for life in a modern industrialized country. The Soviet had inherited from Czarist Russia an educational system closely patterned after that of continental Europe. Qualitatively it was not much below European standards but quantitatively it was totally inadequate. Russia was 60 to 70 per cent illiterate at the outbreak of World War I, but liberal influences had begun to permeate the country and education was being rapidly extended. Perhaps 50 per cent of Russian children were in elementary and 7 per cent in secondary schools at the outbreak of the Revolution. Scientific work of high quality was being done at Russian universities. Had Russian education not been disturbed it would undoubtedly have caught up with that of the rest of Europe in a reasonable length of time.

Once they seized power, the Soviets promptly took control of all schools—public and private—and replaced them with a unified, nine-year labor school which was to be compulsory and open to all children. Since available facilities were woefully limited, admission to school was determined by the political rather than the intellectual worth of the child. Into the schoolrooms and academic halls poured the sons of the proletariat. In fact, for many years bourgeois origin was an absolute bar to education; this was in line with Marxist dogma that schools are tools of the government by means of which those in power perpetuate their control of the state. Protests by teachers that indiscriminate admission of vast masses of children would lower scholastic standards were dismissed as irrelevant. Already suspected by reason of their professional status, the teachers' views on education were brushed aside as bourgeois heresy.

While famine, civil war, and economic collapse forced closing of one school after another, a vigorous debate over the future form of Soviet education went on. In the light of today's monolithic authoritarianism it is strange to read of the wide range of experimentation which took place in Russian schools during the 1920's. Not surprisingly, perhaps, the educational philosophy of John Dewey and the experiments of American progressive educationists found some degree of favor. Evolved in a totally different spirit from that animating the Soviets, American experimentalist theories nevertheless seemed to fit Soviet needs. The Russian Government was engaged in the gigantic task of refashioning the individualistic Russian into collectivist "Soviet Man" and demanded that every agency of the state take part in this mass-reconditioning process. This meant, of course, that the primary purpose of the schools ceased to be transmission of the cultural heritage of the race or teaching minds to think clearly and independently. "The task of the new education," said Lenin, "is to unite teaching activities with a socialist organization of society." Soviet teachers were told they "must consider themselves as agents of communism as well as general education."

Thus education was to be replaced by training; development of young minds by behavioral conditioning. The progressive emphasis on "adjusting" the child to the community fitted right into this new objective of Soviet education. In the United States, too, some of the more extreme leaders of the movement advocated that "teachers should deliberately reach for power," and use it to "definitely and positively influence the social attitudes, ideals, and behavior of the coming generation." Fortunately our teachers have always been more sensible and steadfast of purpose than their more volatile leaders. Nevertheless, a glance at the Marxist version of familiar progressive ideas helps us realize just what can happen when schools are turned from their traditional concern with developing young minds to the progressive objective of conditioning the "whole child"—something very close to propagandizing your children.

Dewey's belief that the school must, "in the first place, itself be a community of life in all which that implies," and that "the measure of worth" of schools "is the extent to which they are animated by a social spirit," found acceptance among some Russian educators. In view of the government's wish that young Russians learn to respect physical labor and that they be willing to become factory workers, these educators tried to make classrooms as much like factories as possible. Neither school desks nor teaching of subject matter is to be found in factories; these, therefore, were eliminated in some schools. Teachers organized school work into "projects" which were assigned to groups of children called brigades. Each such brigade was tested "as a collective" and the youthful leader was made responsible for the performance of his group. There were some Russian educators who felt that in a socialist school even the teacher ought to be a member of the class and have no more authority than the children; everything was to be done in a cooperative way.

Despite the leeway given to experiments in methods of teaching, Marxist dogma on education remained paramount. Education had to be identical for all children since the purpose of education was to produce Soviet Man; political conditioning was more important than presentation of subject matter.

Meanwhile the experienced teachers left over from the old regime were rapidly replaced by unqualified but politically reliable Soviet teachers. Curricula were revised each year. Textbooks had to be continually rewritten to conform with party-line shifts. Young Komsomols and party inspectors broke into classrooms at frequent intervals to check on the political orthodoxy of everything taught. Teachers were ill-paid and overburdened.

This hasty and ill-considered tampering with education went on for fifteen years before its disastrous results became evident to Russia's rulers. Universities and other institutions of higher learning began to complain that the schools sent them students who could not deal with fractions or solve second-degree equations; who had never heard of Newton's binomial theorem; who knew next to nothing of geography and history and because of ignorance of foreign languages could not understand scientific terminology. The whole matter came to a head when it was discovered that the five-year plans would remain blueprints unless Russian schools provided well-trained professionals, technicians, and skilled workers to carry them into effect.

The Soviets thus came up against their first insurmountable obstacle, one which could not be liquidated by propaganda or by force. Either Marxist dogma had to be given up or the plan to transform Russia into a modern industrial state must be relinquished. It was as simple as that. Faced with this dilemma, which must have been painful indeed, Russia's leaders sacrificed dogma and did a complete about-face. They abolished the comprehensive labor school and reinstated prewar curricula and teaching methods.

Because of this willingness to come to terms with facts, Russian education for the past two and a half decades has in reality been European education altered in but two important respects: simplicity and universality.

First, as to simplicity. Russian education is a sort of utility model from which everything considered nonessential by the Soviets has been stripped. Instead of the choice offered by European schools of classical, semi-classical, or mathematics-science education, there is only one basic school preceding higher or university education—the ten-year school. The curriculum is identical in the same grade in every school throughout the country. Its content resembles that of the European mathematics-science school but it has only one compulsory foreign language compared to the usual two or three. The broad general culture and the independence of judgment which European schools develop in their students are lacking. Freedom of the mind is allowed only where the subject matter makes this indispensable.

Second, as to its universality. This has two aspects. In the first place, Russia has gone further than any other country in eliminating the element of cost in education. No Russian child is barred from the highest education because of the poverty of his parents. He not only pays no tuition; the state *pays him* to study. It pays the entire cost of maintaining and educating him for which in return the student must serve three years in any post to which he is assigned. This is not a new idea. France has long granted state scholarships providing free tuition, room, and board to selected students preparing for the teaching profession, on condition that the student sign an agreement to teach for ten years in public schools or refund to the state the cost of his maintenance. The Federal Education Act of 1958 provides that college students may borrow up to $5,000 at 3 per cent interest of which half will be canceled if the student teaches school full time for five years after graduation. The G.I. bill gave outright scholarships, which included tuition and a monthly stipend for room and board. But these instances aside, no state has gone as far as Russia in paying the total cost of education from kindergarten through final professional degree. The result of this huge investment in brain power is that Russia now possesses a large pool of well-trained professionals from which she can select the very best to fill positions requiring not only superior intellect but also prolonged education and training.

The reverse side of the medal is that schooling must be earned by proving competence. The state wastes no money on children who either cannot or will not keep up with their studies. Schooling is not a right of the Russian child. Comprehensive examinations are taken at the end of the fourth and seventh grades; failures are dropped and then go to vocational schools which prepare them for work. Children are under great pressure to study hard, since it is only through higher education that they can achieve a life of relative comfort and decency. The alternatives to hard study are submergence in the gray mass of factory and farm workers and a likely call to army service. Universality of education is therefore combined with rigorous standards which insure excellence—something we have failed to do. Russian education is like European education in this insistence on excellence, but Russia is putting much more money proportionately into schools, libraries, and laboratories than the Europeans, and her political system makes for much stronger motivation than exists in any free democracy.

In comparing the educational systems of different countries, it is important to divest ourselves of political bias, whether *pro* or *con*. A distinction must be made between the *kind* of knowledge and training given in the schools and the *purposes* for which this knowledge and training are subsequently utilized. We can then rid ourselves of emotional propensities and judge the *kind* of education offered by the schools of a given country dispassionately, even though we abhor the *purposes* for which that country educates its children. We can learn from Russian education. We can learn, first of all, that a much larger percentage of children are capable of absorbing an academic secondary-school and university program than we have been led to believe.

To grasp the significance of Russian education we must realize that, Marxist window dressing apart, it is mass education very nearly at the level of excellence of the European upper-track secondary school and scholastically well above the level of the usual American college-preparatory high school.[1] Presently about 15 to 20 per cent of European children pass the entrance examinations to their academic secondary schools and of these around 20 per cent or so drop out before graduating. About 5 to 6 per cent of their age group complete a professional university education. In the United States, 55 per cent of fifth-graders graduate from high school of which hardly a majority have taken a college-preparatory program. Some 25 per cent enter college, and of these about 50 per cent drop out before graduating with a B.A. or B.S. Only 5 to 6 per cent—as in Europe—complete professional educations of the kind which requires a four- to six-year university course abroad. On the basis of the best information we can obtain, it can hardly be doubted that Russia gets 39 per cent of her fifth-graders through the tenth grade and that at least 35 per cent pass the school-leaving examination. A third of these enter universities and institutions of higher learning where the dropout appears to be insignificant. It would seem that 10 to 12 per cent of Russian youth complete professional training—that is twice the percentage in Europe and the United States. For every available place in a Russian institution of higher learning there are three well-qualified aspirants. This raises the standards and insures that the best brains of the country become scientists, engineers, and other professionals. The Russian achievement in education appears to be the result of three factors: lavish financial support of education, excellent teachers, and strongly motivated children.

Most European countries, by 1957–58 figures, put about 2½ to 3½ per cent of their national income into public education; we invest 3½ per cent, or nearly the same; Russia invests more than 6 per cent, and some experts believe it may be nearer 12 per cent. When a country with a much lower living standard than ours spends a greater percentage of national income on education, it is time we pause and reflect.

Russia's education rubles go to teachers and scientific

[1] See Appendix 3.

equipment first, buildings second. However, she has some impressive academic buildings, notably Moscow University. In general, the buildings are old, Spartan, and crowded. The equipment is excellent, as are the library facilities. Russia's educational plant therefore has the essentials. It is an enormously productive plant because it processes all children who are educable. There are no artificial barriers to education, only those set by nature. Elimination of cost is one of three factors which determine the extent to which the potentialities of a people are realized. The other two are the quality of the teacher and the motivation of the student. Russia excels in both. Her teachers are better prepared than ours. They are expected to master their respective subject matter to a degree which makes them scholars in their field, albeit on a modest scale. They are respected and well paid.

More important than lavish expenditures, a cost-free education, and good teachers is the intense motivation of Russia's children. If we are to believe Russian statistics, many students of average ability get through the rigorous ten-year school. This is not surprising, since in the past, when the children of European middle- and upper-class parents went to the tough academic secondary schools as a matter of course, even average children managed to get through by dint of hard work, parental help, tutoring, and occasionally repetition of a school year. Children exerted themselves because the social mores made graduation from these schools the *sine qua non* of middle- and upper-class standing. Without it a person could not obtain a position which would be appropriate to his parents' social standing. Only those few who inherited a large fortune, a business, or an estate could get by with an inferior education. Conversely, a talented poor child could move up the social ladder in few other ways than by an academic education. Something not unlike this kind of motivation seems to induce Russian children to work exceedingly hard, and they also are helped by their teachers who will tutor those who need it. Doubtlessly parents urge them on, too, since they know full well that desirable positions in their socialist society come only to those having a good education. The net effect is to give Russia an abundance of trained man power. Bulganin calls this the Russian "gold reserve."

It is this combination of good scientific equipment, high scholastic standards, good teachers, strongly motivated students, and cost-free education which makes Russian education a formidable challenge to us. Russia also has more land and people than we; her population density is smaller; her natural resources are larger since she controls those of the satellites. As intelligence is probably fairly evenly distributed over the world, it is logical to suppose that a country which develops *all* its intellectual resources will in the long run be stronger than a country which develops only *part* of its intellectual resources. Whether this supposition is invalidated when the first country enslaves its people and the second country is free, we do not know. It seems likely that the defects inherent in a totalitarian form of government will offset some of the benefits obtained from the Russian educational system.

We who do not know what it means to live without freedom believe that the atmosphere of repression permeating a police state must shrivel the human mind and spirit, but we have no evidence that it does so in Russia. It would be safer for us to assume that a well-educated people will have the advantage over an uneducated people and proceed to restore the balance. Unless we remove accretions of ineptitude, irrelevance, and frivolity from American education, we shall be severely handicapped in the "cold war of the classrooms." A school system which *educates* children is better than one which amuses them, conditions them to a life of conformity, trains them to pick the correct tie, the appropriate silverware, or the right mate. It is a better educational system regardless what use is made of its products.

In comparison with the Russian school system ours is not so well financed; education through the professional degree is not cost free; teacher certification and training emphasize *how* to teach; subject-matter knowledge among public schoolteachers is inferior to that of European and Russian

teachers. Most important, strong motivation has never acti-
vated American children. Our land has always been so
bountiful that one could make a good living with little
formal education. This situation is changing. In the near
future population growth, natural-resources exhaustion, and
higher levels of technology will put a premium on the
trained mind. Education which was good enough for our
parents is not good enough for us and will be still less adequate for our children. This would be true even if Russia
did not exist. Her determination to achieve technological
supremacy simply forces us to hasten reforms which we
could otherwise have made at greater leisure. We should
have had to progress technologically but not quite so fast as
competition with Russia now makes necessary.

We cannot progress unless we turn ourselves into more
effective human beings. We must, in particular, make better
use of our minds if we are to live successfully in the artificial
setting created by science. It is the responsibility of the
school to teach children how to make better use of their
minds. If the school fails to do this, it will undermine our
chances of keeping ahead of the Russians. Unfortunately,
we are now harvesting the bitter fruit of an educational
philosophy which has set its aims too low. Life-adjustment
education merely aspires to adjust the child to life as it is. It
does not bring out the potentialities in children which would
change life for the better. It does not produce enough students who are well prepared to become professionals. This
slows the tempo of technological progress. Our achievements
fall short of our potentialities. Our educationists do not seem
to realize that a rising standard of living will in the future
be more closely related to the education of our children. A
country such as ours must depend more and more on persons
who possess trained intelligence; who work competently
with ideas. To raise our gross national product by 3 per cent
annually we must increase scientific and engineering man
power by 4½ to 5½ per cent annually. Fifty years ago we
needed one engineer for every 1,000 workers; now we need
one for every 65, and in some industries one for every 20.

We do not have enough well-qualified engineers. In the atomic-energy program shortage of skilled professionals is the chief cause of delay.

Russia, meanwhile, is reaping a rich harvest from her own investment in education. Her percentage increase in gross national product is currently twice ours, or 6 per cent annually. Again I must caution that figures about Russia are to be taken as educated guesses. But whatever our respective rates of increase, it is certain that Russia advances technologically much faster than we and has much lower lead times. There is no reason why we cannot make as drastic educational reforms as did Russia. We are richer; we do not have to start from rock bottom; we have many qualified persons who could pinch hit while we start training teachers for a more rigorous scholastic program. Our practical problems are not unsurmountable. What holds us up is a lack of public interest, and without public support nothing can be done. A totalitarian government can of course make drastic changes affecting its people without bothering to obtain their consent. That is why in periods of rapid change totalitarian governments sometimes move with greater speed and efficiency than democracies. Since the Russian Government is all-powerful, it can exert more pressure on children to spur them on to maximum efforts than is possible in democratic countries; teacher shortages can be overcome by ordering people into the teaching profession regardless of their wishes; building materials can be diverted from housing desired by the people to buildings deemed more useful to the state—such as schools, laboratories, libraries, universities. Obviously a totalitarian government, once it decides to set up a formidable educational program, can do so more quickly and easily than a democracy.

What concerns me most about the Russian school program is not the coercive element which speeds all totalitarian programs, but the solid evidence that Russia has found a way to inspire in her children the desire to put forth their utmost mental efforts; and that she has done this through what we think of as "capitalist" incentives. A Russian child works hard and examinations are tough. But ahead looms a professional career which is highly attractive, combining excellent salary with much honor, prestige, and respect. Teachers are well paid and highly regarded. Children are imbued with a love of intellectual adventure through books in which the hero is a scientist or engineer who does valiant deeds that will benefit the country—not, as in so many of our books, and even more on radio and television, a cowboy or space cadet. I doubt whether you could find a counterpart in Russia of the one hundred American high-school pupils who were recently queried on why they did not take mathematics and science courses. Their answers reflected disdain for scientists who were described as "squares," "long hairs," and "little men with beards" working in musty laboratories. These youngsters were not interested in scientific or engineering careers because they regarded them as financially unrewarding as well as being too difficult and time consuming.

Because we have no national standards in education, it is difficult to compare our schools with those in other countries. In view of the Russian advances it would be disastrous if we failed to at least make an attempt to do so. We should merely lull ourselves into a false sense of safety if we equated the Russian, or for that matter the European upper-track secondary school, with our high school. We have always overvalued the American high school. Merely because its graduates are approximately of the same age as European graduates of secondary schools, we keep thinking of the two as being, if not identical, at any rate comparable. This would be true only if you equate possession of social poise, good citizenship, and pleasant disposition with solid academic knowledge such as even few colleges in the United States impart in a four-year course.

In recent comparisons of American and Russian education we have, for example, compared the *number* of graduates of the Russian ten-year schools with those of American high schools and found the result not too disheartening. Similarly, we lump together United States college and university enrollment (only 11 per cent of which is postgraduate) and compare it with enrollment in Russian universities and professional schools; again, though not good, the figures are not actually frightening. We carefully count the hours our children spend in elementary and high school and find that in twelve years they have sat in class about the same length of time as the Russians in ten years. We then say sadly that the Russians do seem to get more sciences, mathematics, and languages than our children and that something should be done about it.

We follow the same procedure when we make comparisons with European schools. It comes out that we have many more children in high school and in college than they have in secondary schools and universities, and this makes us proud. All of these comparisons are meaningless because the European secondary-school graduate has learned more than many American college graduates; and as to our high-school diploma, the less said about it the better.

How can you make a meaningful comparison between the American high school and the Russian ten-year school or the European secondary school? The latter two can be compared with each other and the Russian comes out the worse, though not in things which the government considers essential. But one cannot compare the number of hours spent in our high schools with those spent in any European or Russian secondary school, for even the hours are not qualitatively the same. There an hour at school means an hour of uninterrupted serious work; here there are assemblies, errands to be run, special assignments (such as collecting milk bottles for lunch), and the teacher must spend a great deal of time helping the dullards who would so much rather be on the outside earning money than trying to study "language arts." It takes almost a week to get work started at the beginning of each semester and another week to tidy up at the end. Then there are trips to survey various adult activities, checking on the fire department or the bakery, and much time goes into preparing for the school play.

It isn't even possible to compare one hour of French or

physics in the average American high school with one hour
of these subjects in a European or Russian secondary school
and for this reason: over there they have a continuous program of instruction which advances from the moment the
subject is first introduced. As the child grows in understanding the presentation of the subject by the teacher becomes
broader and deeper, more information is added and more
facts are discussed, until in the end the pupil masters the
subject thoroughly and it is his for life. In such a well-
planned program each hour carries the pupil's knowledge a
step forward. But we, in a mistaken idea that the child
should exercise free choice, give him leeway to pick and
choose among a large number of subjects. He may take
French in the ninth grade, drop it for two years, and then
take it up again in the twelfth. Meanwhile, he will have forgotten most of what he learned and time will be wasted re-
viewing in the second year what was supposed to have been
learned in the first year.

A point is reached where quantitative diversity becomes
so great that comparisons are meaningless. The Russian ten-
year school, for example, gives each and every student 1,353
hours of classroom and laboratory instruction in the sciences;
only one third of our high-school graduates have studied science at all, and the maximum instruction obtainable, with a
few exceptions, is 756 hours.

Take foreign languages: every pupil in a European sci-
ence-mathematics secondary school has at least six years of
two foreign languages and many take a third. Yet many of
our high schools teach no foreign languages at all, and there
are few graduates who have had as much as three years of
even one foreign language.

Some American high-school graduates never get beyond
quadratic equations, but every graduate of the European sci-
ence-mathematics secondary school must be familiar with
differential and integral calculus, analytical geometry, application of mathematics to physics, and spherical trigonometry.

It is time we face up to the fact that not many American

students at age twenty-one to twenty-two know as much after a four-year college course as European upper-track secondary-school graduates know at age eighteen to nineteen.

In our pride at the number of American children who graduate from high school we forget how few of them have taken an academic course comparable to that of the academic secondary schools in Europe or of the present ten-year school in Russia. Of the 55 per cent who graduate from high school here, only a very small percentage have learned as much in literature, in their native language, in foreign languages, sciences, mathematics, astronomy, and geography as all of the 39 per cent who graduate from the Russian school.[2] It is evident that our society is such that children are not motivated to obtain a rigorous academic education. It is too easy to make a good living without much of an education. This lack of motivation is dangerous today when the Scientific Revolution is upon us and we need many people with a good liberal-arts background and excellent professional education as well.

I have received many letters from anxious and worried parents. This was gratifying because it gave me hope that something would be done to better our schools. It was not surprising since I expected as much of American parents. What did surprise me was the interest and concern expressed by foreign correspondents. I should like to quote from a letter written me by a Swiss physician, enclosing a long, carefully thought-out essay on the differences between American and European education; written, I may add, in faultless English! The letter said in part: "In sending you the enclosed, I am fully aware of the fact that America is quite capable of taking care of her problems and of solving them to her own satisfaction. But there are so many of us here who love and admire America and we want her to succeed in her attempt to overtake Russia in science and learning. Be pleased to excuse, if some of us seem to have made a friend's

[2] For further comparison with Russian education see Appendix 3.

worries our own. We cannot help it. What we fear is Russia's youth with its simple, austere mode of life and the resulting stock pile of time and energy at its disposal for work and study; its rigorous system of education, borrowed from Central Europe, where most of its scientists and educators come from. Yet all of us here want America to lead in scholarship and scientific achievements. *Do you think that dollars alone will do it?"* (My italics.) I often think of these words when I encounter the easy optimism, the blind complacency, the stubborn refusal to take heed of warnings which are characteristic of so many of our progressive educationists. I think of the time and care expended by a friend of America, a citizen of a small sister republic, in order to send me information that might help in my efforts to bring about awareness of the danger in which we find ourselves because of educational deficiencies.

The danger is well understood by all who know about our man-power shortage. At the conclusion of its lengthy investigation into this shortage, the Joint Atomic Energy Committee remarked in a preface to the Hearings on Shortage of Scientific and Engineering Man Power: "The basic issue is whether or not we as a nation are willing to sit by and watch Soviet Russia, with her vast technical training programs, outstrip us in technological development in the coming years, or whether we take action now to see to it that the United States has the trained man power to insure our continued world leadership in this field. We are in a battle for brain power." These are grave words and Sputnik has underlined them for us. As the committee remarks, the testimony before it "is a shocking indictment of America's indifference toward one of the most serious problems facing this nation."

Basically it is an indifference to intellectual excellence, to matters of the mind. We still think more highly of an athlete than of a brilliant student. We still do not as a people realize that in modern life, as Whitehead said it so elegantly: "The rule is absolute, *the race which does not value trained intelligence is doomed.* Not all your victories on land or at sea can move back the finger of fate. Today we maintain ourselves. Tomorrow science will have moved forward yet one more step, and there will be no appeal from the judgment which will then be pronounced on the uneducated."

Chapter 10

WHAT CAN WE DO?

The past months have been a period of rude awakening for us. Our eyes and ears have been assaulted by the most distressing sort of news about Russia's giant strides in technology, based on the extraordinary success she has had in transforming her educational system. All but in ruins twenty-five years ago, it is today an efficient machine for producing highly competent scientists and engineers—many more than we can hope to train through our own educational system which we have so long regarded with pride and affection.

We are slowly thinking our way through a thicket of bitter disappointment and humiliating truth to the realization that America's predominant educational philosophy is as hopelessly outdated today as the horse and buggy. Nothing short of a complete reorganization of American education, preceded by a revolutionary reversal of educational aims, can equip us for winning the educational race with the Russians.

Ours is a democracy. We cannot move forward faster than the majority of the people will permit us to go. But today the American people are aroused because they realize that something is fundamentally wrong with American education when a country—three fourths illiterate a generation ago—can in twenty-five years catch up with us in so important a field of knowledge as science and engineering. In a race it is of little importance how far ahead you are at the start when your opponent runs faster and the race goes on forever. A head start makes victory more certain only when the race is short.

Anxious parents who sense the ominous overtones of the

188

news about Russian education have asked me: "What *can* we do?" I have also heard from people in all walks of life who do not have children in school but are still concerned enough to want to help and ask me *how* best to go about this. It has not been humanly possible for me to answer all these letters. My work in naval nuclear propulsion keeps me busy seven days a week and leaves me little leisure. For ten years I have hoarded my small amount of leisure and invested it in an effort to understand what went wrong with the American dream of universal education and how we might put it right again. There has been no time to answer letters, nor do I have a staff to help me in this leisure-time activity. I hope the many serious and conscientious people who never received an answer from me will take this chapter as a personal reply to their letters.

It is good to feel that one has friends when the enemies are so multitudinous and vociferous. In the great debate over American education, which started in earnest after the first Sputniks went aloft, there has been much evidence of a sense of outrage against the critics because they uncovered errors in judgment and in performance, and little awareness of the urgency of our educational crisis—little of the true patriotism which puts the larger issue of national survival above personal sensibilities and job security. It is never pleasant to be told that one has not done his job satisfactorily. Most critics have been fair enough to place the blame not on the schools alone but on all of us. None of us is without guilt. But now that the people have awakened to the need for reform, I doubt whether reams of propaganda pamphlets, endless reiteration that all is well with our schools, or even pressure tactics will again fool the American people into believing that education can safely be left to the "professional" educators. If it be true that but yesterday our schools mirrored American mores and pleased most American parents, this is no longer so. The mood of America has changed. Our technological supremacy has been called in question and we know we have to deal with a formidable competitor. Parents are no longer satisfied with life-adjustment schools. Parental objectives no longer coincide with those professed by the progressive educationists. I doubt we can again be silenced. We are in a mood to make ourselves heard. It is tragic for our country that few of those to whom we entrust our children will face up to their past errors and join us in seeking ways to make ours the best educational system in the world.

Too long have we been discouraged from voicing discontent and offering suggestions for educational reform by being told that these are matters for the experts and which we are not competent to judge. This is a most undemocratic argument. In no other respect is democracy so clearly set apart from authoritarian forms of government than in the right and duty of each citizen to check and evaluate the performance of government, and to express his disapproval if public servants do not carry out the mandates of the people. This right and this duty are not limited to citizens having special competence equivalent to that of the public servant so criticized. We may criticize the police if they are derelict in their duties though we have no special criminological knowledge. We need not be tax experts to have strong views on taxation and to make them known in no uncertain terms. Like that of all public servants, my own work is under constant scrutiny by Congress, by my superiors, and by the press. It is work of a very technical character the details of which many of these critics may not fully comprehend, but what they can and do judge is the end product.

We render judgment every day when we buy one service rather than another; one product rather than that of a competitor. We are not interested in the philosophies animating the persons who provide the services or the manufacturers of the goods. We simply judge them by our powers as consumers. This we cannot do with public servants. Almost all of us must send our children to the schools we support with our taxes. We have no alternative; we are "captive consumers." If the end product of public education is unsatisfactory and if there is clear evidence that the reason for this sad state of affairs has something to do with the philosophies of the leaders of American education, then we are entitled to

criticize and demand a change. Our educational leaders have
never received a clear mandate from the American people
to follow the theories of John Dewey and his disciples. We
have never authorized them to change the objectives of formal education from teaching basic subjects to conditioning
children for group life. Let us not be intimidated by claims
of infallibility because of so-called professional status. Let us
not be overly impressed by academic degrees. Not a few
will turn out to have been won by such scholarly doctors'
theses as, "The Technique of Estimating School Equipment
Costs," "A Scale for Measuring Anterior-Posterior Posture of
Ninth-Grade Boys," or "Public School Plumbing Equipment." Whatever their academic worth, such degrees open
positions of influence in the school system which allow their
possessors to decide whether a school will provide a solid
course of study or one which slants the curriculum toward
what one California school calls the "Essentials of Living."
These particular "essentials" turn out to be such things as
how to take care of a home, how to budget one's income, how
to buy the right kind of food, and—not suprisingly, perhaps—
how to make minor repairs to household plumbing.

I should like every American to get into the battle for
better schools. In all fairness I must warn those who are willing to work actively in their local communities that they do
so at their peril. The powerful leaders of American public
education who have a vested interest in continuance of the
status quo, whose jobs may even depend on it, have so far
shown that they are more interested in retaining their positions and justifying their practices than in joining the American people in a thorough reorganization of our educational
system. There are exceptions. Many classroom teachers in
particular are on the side of progress. But power is in the
hands of a relatively small group of men with strong convictions that they alone know how the child grows, how he
learns, what he must be taught. They are adamant in reject-
ing all lay criticism. They deny the need of real reform. Their
very public utterance repeats—as in an incantation—the
"truth" as they see it, "our schools are the best in the world,

the envy of the world." Since Sputnik there has been a slight modification in this article of orthodox faith: "Our best schools are still unequaled anywhere" is the revised version. They have convinced themselves and, in their righteous conviction, they are impervious to facts that call their faith in question. All they will permit you, the people, to do is to give them more money for more of the kind of education we now have.

If they can, they will punish those who publicly take issue with them. We have had an example of this attitude of the educationists. When *Life* and *Time* published excellent articles on American education this year, they naturally had to show that it was in need of reform. *Life* had published but the first of a series of articles when the influential National Association of Secondary School Principals issued a statement to its members containing the following passages: "We know from experience with another magazine a few years ago that *your most effective weapon will be to question the continuation of subscriptions* to the *Life* and *Time* publications *in your school* as long as they have an attitude and policy inimical to education. Also, we suggest that you urge teachers, parents, and citizens to write similar letters to Mr. Larson [president of *Life* magazine]. *Of course, the force of your letter will be discounted if you indicate that you have been advised to write others such a letter.*" (My italics.)

The men who tried to enforce silence on two responsible and important national magazines by using the tax-supported school libraries as a weapon professed great surprise at criticism by the press. They declared virtuously that they had been completely misunderstood and claimed that "some have distorted the statement issued to our members, the principals of secondary schools [forgetting about the teachers, parents, and citizens who had been urged to join the censorship campaign!] as an effort to curb press freedom. Others have even characterized it as an attempt to organize a boycott against the publication!" Well, I believe it would be difficult to consider the action of the school principals'

association as anything but attempted censorship and boycott.

This is not an isolated case. The National Education Association (NEA) is a powerful pressure group which wields
great influence. Education is big business. One of my correspondents discovered this when he sent a short article on
education—mildly critical—to the journal of a school board.
The article had been accepted and set up when the editor
went to one of the many conferences of educationists which
periodically lay down policies for the schools. On his return,
the editor sent the manuscript back because he had come to
the conclusion, he wrote, that "it would do harm" to the
writer since he was a supplier of equipment to the local
schools. If published, the editor wrote, the article "would
seriously affect any future business you might do" with the
schools. He had discovered at the conference that "just now
the public-school men are in a frame of mind that is entirely
antagonistic to even the slightest breath of criticism of the
schools. The technique is to call anyone who criticizes an
enemy of education, and to treat him accordingly."

Finally, it must be understood by all reformers that if they
do succeed in improving their schools these may well, in
consequence, be "disaccredited." Thus, Holland Christian
High School of Holland, Michigan, a small denominational
school whose graduates have long done well at college, was
told last year that its accreditation would be withdrawn unless it instituted courses in home economics and shop. The
threat came from the North Central Association of Colleges
and Secondary Schools which sets the standards for schools
whose graduates are accepted without examination by colleges and universities in that region—nineteen states are included. The reason given was that the school was neglecting
the needs of two thirds of its students who do not go to
college. In this particular community mothers in general are
capable of teaching their daughters home economics, and
shop training is available elsewhere. The community had the
audacity to disagree with progressive notions of what sub-

jects are useful to children and insisted that its school teach languages, mathematics, science, and history.

What gives the case special significance is that this association of educationists is charged with checking the schools in regard to the quality of their *college-preparatory course,* for it is on this course that accreditation itself is based. Instead, we find the association using its power of accreditation trying to blackmail a good school into wasting tax money on courses for which the community sees no need— money which it prefers to put into a good general education for those who do not go to college. The Holland High School authorities promptly voted against cluttering the curriculum with "know-how" subjects and the association just as promptly struck the school off its list of accredited schools. It is to be hoped that the colleges and universities in that region will disregard the action of the educationists and give special preference to students from so valiant a school. Unfortunately, in another case the association succeeded in browbeating a school. The Springfield High School at Springfield, Illinois, complied with educationist dictatorship and "strengthened" its home-economics and shop courses which had been criticized as inadequate by the association.

For champions of better education a hard year is ahead, so the *Wall Street Journal* warns. NEA is girding for a giant counteroffensive and has already upped membership dues from $5.00 to $10.00 to strengthen its legislative activity. The goal is to regain the people's confidence, so largely lost in what is called "a year of infamy." This is to be done not by a change in the progressive theories but by vigorous attacks against "unprofessional consideration of school programs"— in other words, expression of lay criticism of our schools. The counteroffensive is being organized from its elegant headquarters in Washington—as luxurious a home for the top leaders in education as is provided by the more affluent labor unions. I hope no American will let himself be intimidated. The welfare of our children and the future of our country are too important for us to give up the fight before it has made a good start.

There are many things we can do. First, we must study the
problem and do some homework. I have appended a brief
"Primer for Parents," which gives a minimum assignment involving purchase of two inexpensive paperback books which
should be in every home library. Other reading can be done
in your public library. Fortunately we have the best libraries
in the world—wonderful suppliers of the tools for self-educa-
tion. In these we have a mass-education facility which does
not seek to feed us intellectual fare for "life adjustment."
Luckily, the librarian's Dewey had no other objective than
to make it easy to locate books—he devised the finest cata-
loguing system. Put your local library to use and it will be
an aid in bettering your schools.

Control of schools is vested in local school boards. If you
realize that <u>board members</u> have an extremely difficult and
important task, you will campaign for men of superior intelligence, achievement, and character. Average board members will want average teachers who will provide average
learning and the result will be average. Children need intelligent teachers who can challenge their minds; they, in turn,
need principals who are themselves experienced teachers of
high caliber besides knowing how to measure windows and
get people to fix the plumbing. To obtain these you need
school boards whose members are well above the average so
that all along the line there may be progress. I should think
you would want on the board someone with an excellent education who can judge the quality of curricula and textbooks;
a practical man who employs different types of people and
so knows what sort of qualifications will be expected of the
products of our schools. Parents who have earned the respect of the community because of the manner in which they
have raised their children should be represented on the
board and, to make the board run smoothly and efficiently,
perhaps a popular political figure familiar with educational
problems.

Naturally, every community makes up its own ideal slate
and then tries to get the right men, for no school board can
ever be anything but a mirror of the community—it must

have community support, for this is a democracy. Therefore, should yours be a community where few children go to college, there will probably be little interest in college-preparatory courses. But there is this to consider: the comfortable, safe, healthy life led by average Americans is not the product of the efforts of average men. Great and wise political thinkers, clever inventors, patient researchers, devoted humanitarians and many, many professional people have brought it into being. Without them it would soon cease to exist. Should not every community make provision for the kind of schooling which prepares talented youngsters, from whatever home background, for possible service in the ranks of the creators and developers of civilization?

Good education is not cheap. However, an awful lot of money is currently being wasted in our schools. All communities ought to keep track of increases in child population and make early provision for new classrooms, teachers, and equipment. As long as we have a big deficit for proper support of our schools, ought we not to go over every item on our school's curriculum and equipment to check whether they are really necessary for a good school or can be spared, at least for the time being? Courses for vocational, social, and leisure-time preparation are usually more costly than those for mathematics, languages, or even science, despite the need for science laboratories. This is because these know-how courses depend on machinery and elaborate equipment, not on transmission of knowledge from mind to mind. Recently Robert M. Hutchins described one of our better high-school "palaces"—better in the sense of more costly and more luxurious equipment and "educational" installations. It is a high school having five gymnasiums, (one for boys, another for girls, two auxiliary, and one intramural); an auditorium; a retail store; a band and orchestra room, and another for choral singing; a cafeteria with a stage for theatrical productions; a faculty-student lounge; shops for the building trades, automobiles, general industry, graphic arts, electricity, woodworking, machines, and metals; also rooms marked food, clothing, child development, trade sewing, cosmetology, and "living" (sic). There are eight business classrooms, a green-house, a ceramics room, two drafting rooms, a guidance room, a room for a nurse, and another for a practical nurse. And, as Dr. Hutchins remarks: "Of the total teaching area not more than 25 per cent is devoted to anything that could be described as serious learning."

This is, admittedly, an exceptionally elaborate public school, but I venture to say that you can find unnecessary and costly equipment in your own schools as well. Perhaps space is wasted on trivialities which could be put to better use relieving shortages of classrooms where children are taught to spell. Heaven knows they do need to be taught to spell!

The fantastic proliferation of nonacademic courses in our high schools is defended by educationists as necessary to adjust the majority of our children to life and to keep them in school until they are eighteen. Since we have learned how large a percentage of Russian children go through academic secondary schools, I am inclined to doubt that the educationists are right when they say that 60 per cent of American youth is incapable of being prepared either for college or trained for skilled occupations; that only a small minority of students can comprehend abstract mathematics; only a few have either the ability or the need to write and speak with accuracy; and that *we may feel satisfied if we have taught the majority enough reading to comprehend newspapers and magazines "reasonably well."* These statements occur in the *Life Adjustment Education for Every Youth* bulletin of the United States Office of Education (1951). One influential newspaper's comment on this program of life adjustment is that it "bears little resemblance to traditional programs in fundamental skills and intellectual disciplines, but amounts to *making the school a sort of gigantic social-service agency* aimed not at education but adjustment." (My italics.)

I have no "scientific" proof that this is not the real picture. I have only my confidence in American youth—and here I may be prejudiced—that if properly motivated and *competently taught* they can outdo the youth of any land. Life is easy here; good jobs are to be had by uneducated people; parents are indulgent—all this affects the lack of motivation in our children. At least as much at fault is the sentimental atmosphere permeating educationist thinking and writing which want to make the school the mother and father of every American child—teaching him manners, how to brush his teeth, how to dress, how to find a mate, how to buy shoes and safety pins, how to love everybody, and how to be always "one of the gang," a well-adjusted member in good standing. Our schools openly give as their aim the development of "all-around character and not simply scholarly learning," but they simply cannot do all this "conditioning" and also train the children to think for themselves.

Intellectual training can be combined with home training only when schools are residential, as are the famed English "public" schools. In a short school day there is not enough time to do both. I suggest we turn back to the home what is properly the function of the home and permit the public schools to concentrate on what is properly their function—the education of young minds.

Some of the "know-how" courses might at first glance appeal to you as useful. A course in "don't be afraid to use credit" has some use perhaps; or one on how to use the telephone, or how to budget your household money. When you stop to think, you can see that these are simple, everyday problems which anybody can solve for himself if his mental abilities have been well developed through formal schooling. It is far more important to teach fundamental facts and ideas and to help the child to learn to think clearly for himself than to try to anticipate every petty problem he might meet during his adult life and give him courses so he will be well prepared. Basic knowledge and mind development are the objectives of a good school; techniques in applying these to the diverse problems which one meets in life are the responsibility of the individual. If we want self-reliant Americans, able to cope with a difficult technological world, we must not spoon-feed our children.

Your biggest problem will be to find highly qualified

teachers and enough of them. One simple way to make the best use of those you do have is to organize a mother's auxiliary—perhaps voluntary, perhaps paid at moderate hourly rates. It could do for teachers what nurses' aides do for nurses: relieve them of simple routine chores which take up much of their time and thus cut into their productivity as teachers. Roll call, mid-morning milk distribution, cafeteria supervision, chaperoning dances, and other chores of that kind, even correcting test papers, could be done by non-teachers. Everything that is not teaching should be taken off the shoulders of our teachers. In many communities teachers have been burdened with all sorts of extracurricular chores which should be immediately eliminated.

It has been suggested that teachers would be more "productive" if they used television. Various ingenious schemes have already been tried out. These may be feasible with older students as technical aids or when there are not enough teachers. I myself have some misgivings about the use of TV with younger children; they need the warm human contact with a live teacher and ought not to be thrown into a world of machines too early in life.

The suggestions I have made can all be done at the local level, perhaps through the P.T.A.'s or women's clubs. Mothers will, I hope, take the lead in this matter. They are close to the problem and have better opportunities to organize community support.

I think we must reconcile ourselves to the fact that the teacher shortage will not be remedied in the near future. There is, in particular, great need of teachers with thorough knowledge of academic subjects: languages, mathematics, sciences, history, geography, economics, etc. A practical thing you can do now is to canvass your community for people with special competence in any of these subjects who may be able and willing to teach. These will be found primarily among retired people, driven from their lifework by our mechanistic retirement policies but still youthful enough to work. Their experience and the wisdom which comes with age would be an extra bonus. Retired professors and experts

of all kinds, mothers who in a sense become retired when
their children grow up but whose own good college education qualifies them to teach after a short refresher course—
there must be people of that sort in every school district. A
diligent search would undoubtedly turn up much hidden
talent.

Unfortunately this reservoir of teaching talent cannot be
used unless you organize sufficient mass support for a campaign to get your state legislature to change certification
rules. Otherwise your state board of education will prevent
this sensible emergency measure on the ground that even
the most gifted and knowledgeable person with a talent for
teaching may not do so unless he has taken some fifteen to
twenty-four units of "education" courses. Temporary permits
may perhaps be issued, but these are conditioned on the new
teacher's making up the courses required for certification.
State boards of education are usually bureaucratic strong-
holds of progressive education, having close connections
with the professors of education in teachers' colleges who
give the required courses. Albert Lynd, whose book I have
put first on the list in the "Primer for Parents," remarks that
these professors of education have the local boards of education pretty much under their thumb; indeed "they have cop-
per-riveted one of the neatest bureaucratic machines ever
created by any professional group in any country anywhere
since the priesthood of ancient Egypt." In almost all states
no one can become a teacher or principal unless he has taken
a prescribed number of courses given by these professors of
education.

Even-after the new teacher gets his certification and a
job, his indenture to the professors of education does not end
for he must go back again and again during the summers for
more of what Professor Clapp calls "oceans of piffle." His
salary raises depend on more of the same methods courses.
With so lucrative a system firmly installed, it is not surprising that even during a time of national crisis in education,
when teacher shortages are severe, the bureaucracy which
administers teacher certification will not make exceptions.

In an article in the *Atlantic Monthly*—listed in your "Primer" as must reading—the certification racket which strangles American teaching is documented for one state—Florida—taken at random to illustrate a situation rampant throughout the United States. Like many other states, Florida has a law "written by a professor of education, which provides automatic rank and pay raises for teachers who obtain advanced degrees *in education!*" The author remarks that "merit has nothing to do with the teacher's rank and salary." The road block which prevents our teachers from obtaining the excellent training mandatory in all other advanced European countries is, in my opinion, purely artificial. I think any person who feels the call to teaching wants to be the best possible teacher he can learn to be. Abroad, every teacher in the secondary schools—that is, everyone who teaches children from ten or eleven onward—must be thoroughly educated in general subjects and specifically competent in the subjects he teaches. He must also master the pedagogical tricks which facilitate transmission of knowledge to young people. It is necessary to evaluate the relative importance of a broad general education plus deep knowledge of one's teaching subjects on the one hand, and mastery of the methods of teaching on the other. This is the crux of the matter.

In all professions there are certain tricks of the trade without which the most profound knowledge of subject matter cannot be fully utilized. A trial lawyer must pay attention to his appearance, his voice, his psychological insight into other men's minds; he has to be somewhat of an actor. This professional "know-how" is not taught in law schools. It is an art acquired during pursuit of one's profession. In education, pedagogy compares with this "know-how." It admittedly has importance in the early school grades where presentation of subject matter to very young minds will greatly affect their grasp of it. But as the pupil's mind matures, method grows progressively less important. Teacher training everywhere includes pedagogy, but in no other country is so large a part of teacher training devoted to study of methods, so little to knowledge of subject matter.

This excessive stress on study of the tricks of the trade benefits no one but professors who teach these courses. These, indeed, will never lack for students. Certification requirements insure that education courses will flourish and proliferate. Witness the summer catalogue of a large university which lists seven courses in chemistry and five in physics with two professors for each subject; eleven courses in mathematics with twelve professors—23 courses all told in the mathematics and science departments with 16 professors. These are dwarfed by 142 courses in education with 97 professors! Since even a teacher's time has limits, this control over his professional development prevents all but the most self-sacrificing from acquiring as profound a mastery of their subject matter as is required of their confreres abroad. The ultimate loser is the American child.

Here are three actual cases that illustrate the difficulties which you will encounter if you do find local talent among nonteachers who would like to help out in the present national emergency:

A full professor of biochemistry who had taught all his life was retired from one of our leading colleges because of stringent age-limit rules. He would have liked to relieve the acute teacher shortage in his state, but found that he could not teach chemistry to high-school seniors because he was supposedly not equipped with enough pedagogical talent to do so. The seniors were just one year younger than the college freshmen he had been teaching for many years. The point at issue was, of course, not really his ability to teach but his inability to produce the required credits in "education" courses. Thus a state law supposedly insuring that only qualified persons could be teachers was used to exclude from teaching, because of a technicality, a highly qualified person with long teaching experience. To expect this professor to waste his time taking elementary courses in how to teach, after a life spent teaching young people, amounts to bureaucratic arrogance and almost criminal stupidity.

Another case known to me personally concerns the German wife of a college professor. A new course in German was being set up at the local junior college. She applied for the job of teaching beginners' German, but was refused even a temporary teaching certificate by the state authorities on the grounds that she lacked both sufficient general education and the necessary "education" credits. The lady had graduated from a German academic secondary school—in itself equivalent to three years of college—and had then attended an interpreter's school of university rank for three years, graduating *summa cum laude*. In addition to all of this she had taken twenty-four units of graduate study in linguistics at one of our leading universities and had taught there as an assistant in the German Department. Not unnaturally, she spoke German better than any native-born American.

Anyone who has read Chapter 7 of this book or any of the numerous recent public statements comparing American schools with those abroad can but wonder at this fantastic smugness and "isolation by ignorance" from the world of education outside our frontiers. When I last heard from the German lady, the junior college still had no German instructor and the plan to include a German course had to be dropped.

I should like to cap this sorry tale with that of a former head of the music department at the University of Kansas, former professor of music at Northwestern University, founder of the State Teachers College of Music at Milwaukee, former head of a music publishing house, and inventor of a spinet-type piano—Dr. Miessner. After retirement he took a job teaching music in a local school, "on a permit." In the fullness of its wisdom, the state board of education now has ruled that this permit cannot be renewed unless Dr. Miessner takes *five more semester hours of education courses*.

Replying to vociferous protests against his action in this case, the director of teacher training and licensing of the state board of education replied with one of those irrelevancies so typical of the died-in-the-wool progressive educationists: "After all, you wouldn't let an architect pull your teeth." In its own way, this is a classic "educationist" statement which you will encounter in one form or another whenever you try to relieve local teacher shortages by making use of the human resources in your community. States one press comment: "One would have to look at our more bureaucratic trade-unions, with rigorous rules governing such endeavors as which can paint on wood and which can paint on iron, to find a comparison to the regulations under which teachers in many American communities are supposed to operate."

Most state authorities allow wide discretion in employment of teachers who lack *subject* knowledge but, as we have seen, none for those who lack the required "*education*" courses. In a paper submitted by the Educational Testing Service to the Subcommittee on Research and Development of the Joint Committee on Atomic Energy, it was brought out that a person wishing to teach in an elementary school, for example, can enroll in teachers' college without having taken any high-school mathematics and can graduate without having taken any college mathematics. Yet in most states he will meet the requirements to teach arithmetic.

"Education courses" which count toward certification requirements may be such complicated and difficult matters as how to ventilate a classroom properly, how to run a tape recorder, how to teach the art of listening, group dynamics, "nesting" hand-painted tin cans, and classroom democracy. Courses of this kind are made the criterion of "professional" competence in a teacher. So equipped, he is considered qualified to teach *anything*. This uniquely American concept of what makes a teacher leads to such absurdities as the case of one superintendent of schools in a large city who assigned teachers deliberately to subjects they had never studied so that they would become "child centered" and avoid being "subject centered."

The anti-subject-matter bias of educationists can lead to quite astonishing results. In his article, "Education in the Light of the Satellites," Professor J. H. Hildebrand tells of an interesting "project" in a science class taught by a teacher lacking the most elementary knowledge of the subject she had been assigned to teach. The project was about "hard" water. A pupil had been asked to bring a carton of common salt to make the water hard and a package of baking soda to soften it. "Now common salt is not the constitutent of hard water that renders soap insoluble," remarks the professor, "and baking soda does not soften it. The poor child could learn nothing about hard water under the guidance of a teacher ignorant of the chemistry involved." He concludes, "I could furnish case after case of this sort." So speaks an eminent professor of chemistry at the University of California. No doubt if he asked for a teaching appointment he would be found unqualified to teach chemistry in the very school where the hard-water project took place. Just as the retired college professor of biochemistry, the German lady with a *summa cum laude* degree, and the professor of music were prevented by an educationist bureaucracy from contributing their valuable services, while teachers ignorant of all but "education" courses conduct "projects" in science. How are we to meet the challenge of Russian education when all our efforts to bring excellence back to our schools are shackled by the monumental selfishness of blind men?

Here is a field where you, the American voter, can take steps to eliminate an obvious evil in our educational system. Public pressure can induce state legislature to coerce boards of education into relinquishing their iron grip on your teachers. For encouragement in pursuing the good fight I give you the case of Virginia. Something of great potential importance to American education happened there quite recently. Public opinion operating through the General Assembly forced the state board of education drastically to cut the number of "education" credit hours for teachers and to increase those required in "subjects" such as English, mathematics, sciences, and languages. A liberal-arts college graduate now needs but nine "education" credits to teach in high school. This in itself is a fine thing, but what really makes the Old Dominion a true pioneer for excellence in education is the new rule that even this nine-credit requirement may be waived by the state superintendent in cases where local communities wish to retain the services of retired professors and others qualified to teach who lack these "education" credits. If Virginia can do it, so can your state, if you will but labor patiently, rally public support, and move on the state legislature.

The United States Army has an active program for preparing retired officers to become science and mathematics teachers—currently our most serious deficit area in teaching. This is the Army's reply to a research study of the National Education Association in 1957 which showed that we have only one third the high-school mathematics and science teachers we need. Commenting on this practical and enlightened step taken by the Army, the New York *Times* of May 23, 1958, remarked somewhat skeptically: "Now it remains to be demonstrated whether the various teachers' organizations will cooperate with—or, on the trades-union closed-shop principle, will move to obstruct—those educational authorities who may wish to relieve shortages in the departments of science and mathematics with availables from this new and exceptionally qualified source."

As a temporary relief measure, I suggested some three years ago that we enlist the aid of industry. Why cannot the scientists and the engineers employed by industry be given sabbatical leave to teach in our schools? It is not farfetched to expect industry to help carry this social obligation. In present-day America the business corporation is not a business device alone—it has become a social institution and has acquired the obligations inherent in this concept.

We have always recognized a duality in our schools: federal and local support; public and private support. Industrial support of schools fits into this duality.

It has also been characteristic of our people that when a social need arose which government was not able to take care of, citizens have joined together to help. The program suggested will not, I am certain, fail because of unwillingness on the part of industry to make this significant sacrifice. It may, however, founder on the unwillingness of our educationist bureaucracy to make the infinitesimal sacrifice required of them, that is, to allow qualified men without "education" credits to teach during this national emergency.

I hope this suggested program of action will prove helpful. In the next chapter you will find two more ideas I submit for your consideration. These would involve fairly drastic changes in our school system and require great effort to accomplish. The ideas discussed in this chapter require action merely on the local and state level. Doubtless you will be able to think of many other ways to influence your schools to improve curricula and teaching.

It matters not whether you agree with my views on education. What matters is that all citizens get into the good fight to make our education the best in the world. Debates on facts or ideas are useful for they clarify the issues. Such debates must always be the preliminaries of far-reaching reform. We do not operate by executive, legislative, or "professional" fiat. We are a democracy. Now that we have been aroused to the dangerous effect which poor education has on our strength and influence as a world power, let not men of little vision with their soothing words hold back our righteous anger. We must sweep clean the temple of learning and bring back quality. For, as former President Sproul of the University of California warns us: "If we fail in our hold upon quality, the cherished American dream of universal education will degenerate into a nightmare."

Let us each make a beginning, however small. It takes but the moving of a single pebble to start an avalanche.

Chapter 11

DEMONSTRATION HIGH SCHOOLS AND
NATIONAL STANDARDS

Talented children are this nation's reservoir of brain power. We have neglected them too long. We must devise ways to discover them at an earlier age and to educate them better than we do at present. The first step is to investigate what the top 15 to 20 per cent of our children could accomplish if they were placed in schools designed to fit their particular abilities. Too many now drop out and miss the satisfaction of a challenging professional career which might have been theirs; worse still, they are lost to the nation. I suggested three years ago that twenty-five demonstration high schools be set up in various sections of the country to test the advantages of separate education for the talented. I proposed that this be a private undertaking—at least at first; that industry, labor, and the educational foundations take on the responsibility of showing the way to improve secondary education by setting up such demonstration high schools. The schools would comprise the junior-senior high-school program, endeavoring to complete it in four years instead of the present six. They would be free, but admission would be based on successfully passing a comprehensive examination. Promotion would be by merit alone. The schools would be staffed by teachers of above-average intelligence and training, for an average teacher cannot successfully teach an above-average student. Qualifications for the teachers would include pedagogic skill as well as a broad general education and thorough mastery of one or two subjects. They would compare with European secondary-school professors whose competence, based as it is on years of postgraduate university study in their fields, is one of the main reasons why these

208

teachers can teach more in twelve years than ours do in fourteen to fifteen years.

Teachers in the demonstration schools would be given no extracurricular work, because a teacher, as does any professional person, requires time for thought and study. The schools would be scholastic institutions, so social activities would be kept at a minimum. Teachers' salaries would be in accord with the high scholastic qualifications required and, therefore, equal to those paid for comparable positions in industry. Such salaries would attract competent teachers. These schools should aim at a ratio of at least one teacher for every twenty pupils. One of the reasons why the private English boarding schools, such as Eton, Harrow, etc., contribute so large a percentage of England's leaders is their ratio of teachers to pupils—one every twelve students. The smaller a class, the more can be accomplished by teacher and pupils. Such education is expensive, but no more expensive, I venture to say, than some of our overelaborate vocational installations in high schools of the kind described by Dr. Hutchins.[1] We know what can be achieved with small classes, but we have preferred to put money into elaborate buildings rather than paying the necessary teachers. Outstanding liberal-arts colleges in America have made their admirable records with the favorable ratio of about one to twelve. And, lest we forget, Russian schools now average one teacher to every seventeen pupils; compare this with our ratio of one to about thirty.

The principal purpose of these demonstration schools would be to show that a broad liberal-arts education can be obtained, at least by academically inclined students, in about fourteen years. This would include the entire junior-senior high-school liberal-arts sequence which more and more of our professional schools now require for enrollment. To do this it might be necessary to provide a choice: students could complete the junior-senior high-school course in five years, or they could finish in four years by taking extra

[1] See Chapter 10, page 196.

courses during three summers. We must find a way for our
children to attend school for more than the present 180 days.
Originally, the school year was only 90 days. This made
sense when we were an agricultural country and children
were needed to work on the farm. Today knowledge advances at geometric rates and we cannot afford to have
our children devote only half the days of the year to schooling. Lengthening the time in school might most easily be
done through the medium of voluntary summer courses
carefully fitted into the whole secondary-school program.

The management of the demonstration schools, qualifications and salaries of teachers, entrance requirements, curricula, and standards should be left to an independent body
not connected directly with the donor. I see no reason why
the schools could not be given names to indicate the corporation, or industry, or labor organization which contributes financial support. This seems to me fair and legitimate,
and even desirable; it would win friends for labor and industry as a whole, and for the donor in particular.

I estimate that the cost of operating each model school
for a period of five years would be about ten million dollars.
At the end of that period the community ought to have an
option to take over the school, provided it agrees to continue
the high scholastic standards set under private management.
These schools would demonstrate what could be accomplished by competent teachers, a proper curriculum, and an
adequate school year.

In testimony before the Joint Congressional Committee
on Atomic Energy two years ago, I explained that these
schools would be working examples and goals to any community of what could be done for the education of its children. This demonstration high-school program is something
which could be started at once and would produce in the
quickest possible time professionals trained in the humanities as well as in the sciences and mathematics. I am personally more familiar with the latter and feel particularly
concerned about the time we waste before giving youngsters
advanced mathematics and sciences. A man's best produc-

tive work in science and mathematics usually begins early in life and lasts for a relatively short time. The sooner a young man is ready to forge ahead on his own, the longer will be his productive time and the greater his potential contributions. Mathematics teachers are in very short supply and our mathematics teaching is unimaginative and often out of date. This is a field of knowledge in which the general public usually feels lost. The man in the street does not readily see the "usefulness" of higher mathematics. Yet, unless all intelligent children get higher mathematics in college-preparatory courses, we cannot identify the youngsters with potential mathematical talent. They must be taught the subject in their early teens in order to master it by their early twenties. *Fortune* magazine reports that Russian mathematicians have concentrated enormous effort on the theory of nonlinear equations. To most people this would seem a most unprofitable concern with an abstraction of no obvious use; but, continues *Fortune*, "One consequence is that the Russians are now ahead of the rest of the world in the study of automatic control and *this may account for much of their success with missiles.*"

The advantage of separate college-preparatory schools over separate college-preparatory tracks in our huge "omnibus" schools is that they remove the serious students from the atmosphere of trivialities and easy school life to one where everyone is concerned with matters of the intellect. Of course physical training, music, and art would be included in the academic curriculum. The students would be no more one-sided "odd balls" than are the students at Eton or in the academic secondary schools of Europe. True, they would do a considerable amount of homework and less sitting in the bleachers cheering the school team. Certainly no whole day would be taken off to teach them to be better cheerleaders as was done recently in one city when high-school studies stopped in order that "the level of cheerleading" could be improved.

Talented children are naturally happiest when they go through school with children of similar mental capacity—

their "peers" mentally, but not, let it be emphasized, socially or economically. As it is with adults, children like to associate with others who speak their language and who have similar interests. In homogeneous groups they will act the same as all normal children: full of fun and as interested in athletics and in social activities as any other children. Such children will benefit as much as all others by living through their teens in association with youngsters from different home backgrounds. Children are normally devoid of snobbishness, and this is particularly true of talented children. They will be able to feel free to be themselves in an atmosphere congenial to their kind. In the comprehensive school, many a talented student feels odd and a misfit without knowing that the reason for this feeling is as much his own superior mind which makes him stand apart as it is the average mind of his classmates.

One of the most absurd educationist shibboleths is fear that grouping children by ability will create an elite. There is little danger that intellectual excellence will ever be so highly rewarded in this country that it would create an intellectual elite. Meanwhile this attitude among leaders in American education perpetuates the loss of talent and results in a shortage of trained professional man power. This shortage is a result not merely of the dropout of potentially able youngsters who have become bored with study in our slow-moving comprehensive school but also of youngsters who do not continue their education because of the inordinate length of time it takes to get through preprofessional or general education. Our talented children need not only special school programs which challenge their fine minds, but they also must be allowed to get through school at their own fast pace.

This consideration is almost always left out when our educationists plan special programs for gifted children. Many educators have indeed made the "needs of the talented" their lifework, but what comes out of their numerous researches is seldom more than some form of "enrichment." The difficulty is that talented children do not fit into the life-adjustment pattern. As the *Bulletin* of the Council for Basic Education (March 1958) remarks, the reasoning of educationists runs about like this: "Of course, the 'fortunate deviates,' as we sometimes refer to them, are the subject of exaggerated concern right now, but *we* have always been concerned with them. We have experimented for years with acceleration, parallel classes, homogeneous grouping, but especially with 'enrichment.' We can advance no empirically valid, scientific, thoroughly researched conclusions as yet, but we *are* aware of enormous problems." We can be thankful for the awareness, but, as the *Bulletin* puts it, nothing gets done since "the chief obstacle the professionals can't seem to conquer is their own mythology of the common man and their grotesque fear that special attention to the gifted will create a special social class. The 'literature' of the subject is filled with such unexamined assumptions. For instance, the term 'intellectual elite' inevitably makes its appearance wherever gifted children (one must never call them superior) are discussed. Education is plagued with shibboleths like this one, and they sound impressive enough until one takes a second look and tries to decide what exactly they mean."

Demonstration schools are not, after all, a "revolutionary" idea. The Bronx School of Science is a school rather like the ones I have in mind except that it does not accelerate. New York once had an excellent three-year public high school, the Townsend Harris School, for students capable of completing the regular high-school course in this shorter time. We have many special schools for the handicapped; we have tax-supported special schools for officers in our armed services to which enlisted men do not go. Theoretically, we admit to college only students with above-average minds while others may go perhaps to a trade or a vocational school. Placement of students in schools according to aptitude is not unknown in this country. However, the idea has been violently attacked. The model or demonstration schools are invariably called "elite" schools—a term never used by me and undoubtedly chosen by educationists for semantic reasons to damn them by their very name. I find it hard to see anything undemocratic in this plan. Switzerland is a much older democracy than we, a prosperous country with no special privileges for any particular "elite" class, yet she has her academic secondary schools for children who have the capability to attend them; her vocational schools for those not destined for professional careers.

My proposal has led to at least one major corporation expressing willingness to finance such a school. There was enthusiastic response on the part of the prospective principal and teaching staff but, when last heard of, the whole program had foundered because of opposition by the superintendent of schools of the city in question who considered it undemocratic. Perhaps in the slightly chastened mood of the post-Sputnik era, when many educationists are nimbly scrambling on the bandwagon and now proclaim loudly their desire for better education—perhaps now some demonstration schools will actually be set up somewhere in the United States.

American educational institutions are characterized by a diversity of academic standards without parallel in the world. This is so because we have no over-all agency which requires honest labeling of educational documents. The federal government protects the American people against merchandise which is mislabeled as to quality of content, but no one protects us against schools which are misnamed—colleges that are hardly better than secondary schools; high schools that provide for the majority of their graduates barely more than a prolonged elementary and vocational education; grade schools that operate during the first or second year on the kindergarten level.

No one protects the student who has won his degree for serious college-level work against thousands of degree holders who have gotten by with snap courses. What are we to think of the standards of a university that permits a football star to earn a college degree on a course consisting for one semester of: three hours automobile safety and driving education, three hours of *advanced* automobile driving education, two hours of guidance in secondary education, and one hour of swimming? This is commercialism rampant; academic education dishonored by a desire to exploit talented young athletes for the amusement of the public and in order to gain financial support for the school.

No one protects the teacher who puts in hard work mastering a difficult academic subject against competition from other holders of official "certificates" who are paid the same salary for teaching students to cook or to catch a fish. Those who coach the football team actually get *more pay* than a teacher of, let us say, physics. Do we value our own entertainment above that of educating our children properly? We have abolished child labor in the mines but we encourage it on the football field. So highly do we honor the teachers of school teams that in one state—Florida—60 per cent of the school principals are former coaches!

As an engineer, specifications are second nature to me. I know that standards tend to slip unless an outside agency makes them obligatory. Every item that goes into an atomic submarine has rigid specifications set by us and which industry must meet. Ours is the only major country where the public through its government does not set academic standards. The setting of national standards for teacher training and for the competence which graduates of every type of school must demonstrate before receiving a diploma or degree has always been the first step toward creating and maintaining an excellent educational system. In many European countries the schools are supported by the local community; often the teachers are chosen by a local school board from among all applicants—sometimes, as in Switzerland, after an examination. But the *standards* of teacher training, of school achievement, and of the worth of a diploma are set nationally. These are considered matters for experts—matters devoid of political implications. Experience over many years—in fact, an educational tradition going back to the beginnings of Western civilization—has found the liberal-arts course the best training for young minds whether on the highest level or on a modest level, as for those who complete only the least demanding kind of schooling.

England, where schools traditionally were local and private in nature, has now achieved universal standards which are first-rate. She has done this by granting financial aid to schools through the national government on condition that they maintain standards which school inspectors check from time to time. Beginning with the first shilling of tax money given to education, standards have gradually been raised and made uniform. The process has been slow and, because of its slowness, England completed reorganization of her public educational system a hundred years later than many continental European countries.

We lack a national agency to set standards for school curricula and teacher qualifications. We have convinced ourselves that to hold local schools to national standards of excellence means federal tyranny. We do need federal aid for the schools but everyone clings to the outworn shibboleth that nothing must ever be done by any federal agency to introduce honest labeling into education. Every educational institution sets its own standards. The public elementary and secondary schools are controlled and largely financed on the local level and any kind of outside influence has always been stoutly resisted; even state control is tolerated with ill grace. There is, therefore, no national standard for the high-school diploma. It is granted for educational efforts so dissimilar as to be valueless in judging a graduate's competence. Testifying before the Senate Labor and Public Welfare Committee the secretary of the National Education Association—chief professional association and lobby of public-school educators—admitted that some (sic) schools do not hold high enough standards now, but declared firmly he "would not be able to assent, as the spokesman for the National Education Association, to the proposition that there should be nationwide standards." The reason given was that such standards "would arouse tremendous opposition among our local and state educational authorities"—that is among the men who have foisted on us both the pernicious certification system, which artificially preserves a perpetual teacher shortage in the very fields where the nation most needs good teachers, and life-adjustment curricula.

High standards for American education might lead to some technological unemployment but is there anyone in this dynamic country who can force the people to guarantee him absolute security against technological unemployment? Standards would make their way slowly. It would be an immeasurable gain if we but stopped at once training *future* teachers of frivolities and concentrated on training teachers of solid subjects, while leaving present teachers in the positions they now hold. Ours is a mobile society. People constantly move from one part of the country to another. It makes no sense to have school-curricula and teacher-certification rules which differ from state to state, or even from school district to school district. Children sometimes lose school time when the parents move because they lack locally prescribed credits—such as completion of a course in state history before national or world history may be taken. In a case known to me time was lost because typing had to precede stenography in one state and vice versa in another. I feel sure we would have had an "interstate education" clause in our Constitution, had public education then been prevalent, for does this not have as much or more justification than federal control over "interstate commerce"? After all, the products of local schools move across state lines. Pockets of inferior education endanger us all. We are one country and one people.

Equal diversity prevails among our colleges and universities. Some hardly deserve to be rated as secondary schools while others are excellent, among the best in the world. The B.A., M.A., and Ph.D. degrees which they award are as dissimilar in value as are the diplomas of our high schools.

Only the professional degrees—those given to lawyers, doctors, dentists, and so on—maintain a fairly uniform standard, and it is good. The reason for this unexpected respect for excellence in professional degrees is usually to be found in some form of outside pressure, such as the need to meet state qualifications for licenses to practice the profession. Yet here, too, national standards would be preferable.

Because of the uninhibited manner in which institutions of widely divergent academic standing award diplomas and degrees, it has always been difficult to judge American education by comparing it with that of countries having a similar civilization. Throughout the world the American degree has no assured standing but is judged solely by the reputation of the institution that awards it. This makes it difficult to evaluate the American B.A., especially since nothing exactly like it exists in Europe.

There is much dissatisfaction with our schools today. Parents often feel vaguely that the local high school is below par but they have no way of proving it. In some fashion we must devise a way to introduce uniform standards into American education. Because of the widespread distrust of the federal government in educational matters and the fact that education is constitutionally within the province of the states, I proposed two years ago that we set up a private agency, a council of scholars, financed by our colleges and universities as a joint undertaking or perhaps by foundations. This council would set a national standard for the high-school diploma as well as for the scholastic competence of teachers. High schools accepting this standard would receive council accreditation, somewhat on the order of the accreditation given medical schools and hospitals. Teachers would receive a special certificate if they completed the requisite course of studies. As with my proposal for demonstration schools, the setting of national educational standards would also be a private and voluntary program. My hope is, of course, that if these private efforts succeeded, our public schools would adopt them.

It is most unlikely that, even if they wished to do so, our institutions of higher learning could expand as fast as the student population knocking at their doors. Many colleges prefer to remain small in order to avoid sacrifice in quality.

In consequence, the colleges and universities are now in a position to raise the level of secondary-school education by raising their own admissions requirements. Though the public schools resent having to submit to college admissions, standards and educationists are vociferous in declaring that the public-school system is separate and self-contained, parental pressure cannot be wholly disregarded. In a sense, the private standards set up by the College Entrance Board already perform the function of the secondary-school-leaving examinations abroad. It would be but one step for the council of scholars proposed by me to team up with the College Entrance Board and use the latter to determine whether any school or teacher had actually complied with council accreditation requirements. The board already administers the Advanced Placement Program.

The council of scholars would also soon have at its disposal an authoritative study for a model elementary and high-school curriculum. I refer to the proposed Basic Curriculum Study which the Council on Basic Education now has in preparation. The study is financed by the Relm Foundation of Ann Arbor, Michigan, to a total of $34,000. The council itself is a nonprofit educational organization, composed of persons of scholarly bent and attainment who are united in their conviction that "only by the maintenance of high academic standards can the ideal of democratic education be realized—the ideal of offering to all children of all the people of the United States not merely an opportunity to attend school, but the privilege of receiving there the soundest education that is afforded any place in the world."

The council publishes a monthly bulletin from which I have quoted frequently in this book. An exceedingly well-written and informative running commentary on the educational scene, this pamphlet acts as a gadfly to keep educational defects always before the public eye, and as a strong supporter of every slightest evidence of improvement in our educational performance. From the start, the council planned to issue statements by eminent scholars that would "explain the importance of the basic subjects and set forth what knowledge and understanding a student ought to be equipped with at the end of twelve years of public schooling —that would, in short, describe what basic education *is*." An outstanding scholar in each of the basic subjects will set forth what, in his opinion, should be the proper educational aims of the public school. The fields to be covered will be American history, European history, political science, English composition, literature, classical languages, modern foreign languages, geography, mathematics, biology, chemistry, and physics. In addition to these scholars, other persons representing more general interests in education will prepare papers: a school board member, a representative from industry, and a school administrator. One or two European educators will be present when all these contributions are discussed at a conference arranged by the council. From this cooperative effort the council will then issue a book containing an outline of basic education through the twelve public-school grades.

This book could well be made the starting point for my proposed council of scholars, or they may prefer to undertake their own curriculum study. The important thing to my mind is that we adopt the European method of maintaining high scholastic standards through definitive rules concerning the secondary-school-leaving certificate—here the high-school diploma. Such standards must inevitably be set by authorities outside the public schools and in a sense above them; that is, by those who must deal with the products of American public education. To keep the work of an organization or institution up to the desired level, there must always be an authoritative outside censor of one kind or another. Thus the colleges which make up Oxford or Cambridge University are independent in almost every respect, except that it is the university which confers the academic degree and thus controls the scholastic standard. The European universities control the secondary-school-leaving certificate by refusing to accept students who do not possess the requisite knowledge to pass the final examination; they do not otherwise interfere in affairs of the secondary schools.

Similarly, our own Navy sets definite standards of performance to which every contractor must conform on pain of having his products rejected; the Navy does not otherwise become involved in the affairs of these industries. There is nothing new in this idea.

The present educational chaos that renders American degrees inherently valueless exists simply because up to now we have not had a central authority which sets uniform standards. It is not necessary to make these standards compulsory. We could not do this in our country. All we need is a measuring stick by which to judge the performance of our public servants, the teachers and educationists. Nobody forces them to live up to acceptable scholastic standards, but neither should they continue to be permitted to hide these under life-adjustment verbiage or by threatening dire consequences when anybody—whether layman or educator —presumes to tell the American public the facts about our educational deficiencies.

Community pride would be a potent factor in inducing high schools to obtain accreditation. For the first time parents would have a gauge by which to measure their schools. If the local school continued to teach "life adjustment" and "how to know when you are really in love," instead of trigonometry, French, and physics, its diploma, for all the world to see, would be inferior. Taxpayers will begin to wonder whether they are getting their money's worth when they see other schools receiving accreditation, and when their children find admission to college difficult because of an inferior diploma.

Schools would soon discover that to obtain the coveted accreditation they would have to have teachers with a thorough knowledge of their subjects. This would put pressure on state authorities to bring their teacher-certification requirements into line with today's need for teachers who have a thorough background in the subjects they teach. Another most desirable effect would be the enviable position in which council-certified teachers would soon find themselves. There would be lively bidding for their services with a good chance that their salaries and prestige would rise. More intelligent people would then be drawn into teaching, thus starting an upward spiral and giving teachers at last the true status of professionals which they most surely deserve.

As soon as this proposal was made, it was vehemently denounced as "revolutionary," "unconstitutional," "dictatorial," and so on. I can see no danger of federal control in an entirely private system of accreditation, based on voluntary acceptance and with no legal sanction to back it up. It is merely a method which would establish desirable standards, suggest these standards to schools and teachers, and grant those who accept them a sort of medal—accreditation. Council accreditation would be the one and only American academic certification which represented a clearly defined standard of excellence known and understood by the American people. Council members would be private persons wielding no "dictatorial" powers—men entirely outside the public-school system or the government—scholars who understand the educational needs of a country such as ours, who themselves instruct the products of our public-school system and find them wanting, and who can plan study programs in an impersonal spirit. We would thus have a private agency awarding private labels attesting to a particular kind of fixed and well-known quality of content—"United States choice."

Those who now refuse to consider this or any other method for setting high and uniform educational standards for American public education may perhaps think differently if they take the trouble to study the English public educational system with its slow and patient establishment of national standards. Or, for that matter, the educational systems of the advanced European countries where education is freer than here from unintelligent or bigoted interference; where teachers have more leeway in arranging their teaching materials; but where uniformity of excellence is assured by control over but two items: teacher training and the competence required of graduates before diplomas are awarded them. Only mediocrity has reason to fear the establishment of national standards I suggest.

Within the next fifteen years twice as many youngsters will clamor for admission to our institutions of higher learning. Colleges and universities are now being exhorted to prepare for the flood, and they are criticized when they refuse to expand in order to become mammoth high schools where overgrown children must be taught to spell or write a simple essay, where hardly anyone really knows a foreign language, and many are mathematically illiterate yet confidently expect to become engineers because this is a profession where much money is to be made.

We are in our present predicament because education in America has deteriorated in quality for lack of standards. You can send your boy to college to study fly casting or advertising layouts; your daughter to study etiquette and how to be a hostess. After twelve years in elementary and high school, four years at college, and a minimum of three years of postgraduate study, the student's crowning achievement may be a Ph.D. thesis on "A Study of School Postures and Desk Dimensions." It matters not whether you take courses in calculus, medieval history, women's styles, or interior decorating. Everything is grist to the American educational mill. "You, too, can have a degree." Every American child has the God-given right to march in a commencement procession, clad in mortarboard and academic gown, the rolled-up parchment degree clutched in his hot little hand. What for centuries was a solemn moment crowning long years of arduous mental discipline and hard work has now begun to mark the end of high school and may someday reach our little sixth-grade scholars.

We must rebuild our educational system. To do this we must tackle the many problems in many ways. One is elimination of useless frills. Another is greater effort to improve the teaching of average children in order to bring them to the level which properly motivated average children attain in Europe. Another is to find the right education for our talented children. Let us pay no attention to slogans, clichés, and shibboleths which seek to paralyze action. Let not apathy weaken our momentum. We must have education strong in purpose, versatile in methods, and dedicated to development of citizens who are able to meet the obligations which today's events place upon us. We have the ability to do this. We are rich enough to do this. All we need is the will to do it and to recognize that "the inevitable comes to pass through effort."

PRIMER FOR PARENTS

The first step for those who want to join actively in the campaign for better schools is to do a little homework and acquire a thorough knowledge of our present educational problems—what caused them and how they can be overcome. This is not a particularly difficult subject and one does not need to be a professional expert to understand it. Your librarian can probably prepare a better reading list for you, but here is something to help you get started.

My first suggestion is to invest $2.45 in two paperback volumes which, in my opinion, give you reliable information for a small outlay of cash. They should be in every home library. The first is *Quackery in the Public Schools* by Albert Lynd (Grosset's Universal Library, 1953, $.95). Mr. Lynd has had an opportunity to look at American education from four different viewpoints. He has been a college teacher and knows, therefore, what deans of admission expect of applicants: completion of a four-year program of academic subjects, ability to spell correctly, write grammatically, express themselves intelligibly, and handle mathematics above the level of arithmetic. These seem to be modest qualifications but they are often lacking in otherwise well-qualified applicants. Hence, many remedial courses—sometimes elementary—in English and mathematics have to be given in colleges today. Needless to say, such remedial courses never had to be given in colleges in the days before John Dewey. Mr. Lynd knows what constitutes an adequate college-preparatory curriculum and insists on such a program in the schools of his own community. He is also a businessman and thus has had the same trouble finding qualified employees among today's high-school graduates as have most other businessmen. Qualifications which used to be taken for granted among young men and women who had taken the less academic, more vocationally oriented courses in high school are becoming quite exceptional. There are altogether too many young people today who have not learned at school how to concentrate on their task and do it neatly and properly, how to read simple technical instructions, or how to spell correctly—this latter is a great tribulation to employers of secretaries! Every businessman knows that standards have steadily fallen. Mr. Lynd has also been an active member of his local school board and has had occasion to get to know the people who come from the teachers' colleges imbued with progressive ideas of remaking society through the school. He has the old-fashioned notion that schools should rather concern themselves with teaching the children basic subjects. As a parent, he has the products of our school system under his eyes every day.

Mr. Lynd's book gives you a good survey of the whole problem. It is written in a sprightly manner but its content is solid. He has strong likes and dislikes. He has little use for the progressive educationists but favors higher salaries for teachers, better curricula, and federal aid to the schools. For those who wish to pursue the matter further, he gives references to many other good books and articles.

The Government Printing Office in Washington, D. C., will sell you for $1.50 the *Hearings before the Subcommittee on Research and Development of the Joint Committee on Atomic Energy of the Congress,* held in April and May 1956, on "Shortage of Scientific and Engineering Man Power." This is a volume packed with dynamite. It has almost all the pertinent information on the disastrous man-power shortage which results from our inadequate educational system. Conditions have not improved since it was published. There is, unfortunately, no index. To help you find some of the most interesting items I am listing them below with the page number where the discussion begins:

Comparison of American education and education
in England .... p. 249
Scientific training in England .... p. 249
Senator Benton's report "The 'Cold War' of the
Classrooms" .... p. 32
     with detailed description of Russian education p. 413
Information on Russian education .... p. 328, 338
Statement of representative of the National Science
Foundation on scientific training in the United States p. 47

To keep you advised on what is happening in American public education—the horrors and the hopeful signs—you cannot find a better and quicker guide than the small bulletins published each month by the Council on Basic Education, 725 Fifteenth Street, N.W., Washington, D. C. The cost of subscription is $2.50 per annum. The council is a nonprofit organization of eminent educators who seek to improve our schools by advocating concentration on basic education—languages, mathematics, sciences, etc. Their monthly bulletin is well written and timely. Its descriptions of occasional victories for good education will encourage you and perhaps suggest ideas you could try in your own community.

In view of the destructive effect of the certification system on the quality of teacher training, I suggest that you read at your library an article in the April 1958 issue of the *Atlantic Monthly*, "What Strangles American Teaching: The Certification Racket," by Lydia Stout. The July 1958 issue of the magazine has a rebuttal by a professor of education which reiterates the usual educationist theories in the usual purple pedagogese and with the usual cavalier disregard for grammatical rules.

There are, of course, a great many other good books on the subject, but I am mindful that parents are busy people so I would be quite satisfied if you completed the above listed homework. For those who want to go into the matter more thoroughly there is no better general work than Arthur Bestor's, *The Restoration of Learning* (Alfred A. Knopf, 1955, $6.00). You should make every effort to get this book into your public library. Professor Bestor is one of the first educators courageously to have uncovered the deplorable state of education in the United States. His book is scholarly, thoroughly documented, well written, and, despite its length, will hold your attention. There are innumerable references to other books and articles where you can find more details on specific questions. You will get more out of reading this one big book than by looking through any number of others that have recently appeared, many of which are very good. Professor Bestor's book has never, to my knowledge, been refuted by the educationists in any point, though he has received plenty of brickbats.

This list will give you a start, and you can go on from there without further help.

You will undoubtedly be told by the educationist experts that they "know" how much children can learn, how fast they can learn, and that children are harmed if pushed too fast. There is an enormous amount of "research" going on about the most piffling items which any sensible mother knows by instinct: all of it in the name of "science." So that you will be able to offer concrete examples of what children actually do learn elsewhere, I am adding a brief description in Appendix 2 of the Dutch academic secondary-school curriculum, and also a note on the Russian schools in Appendix 3.

THE DUTCH SECONDARY SCHOOLS
AND A NOTE ON DUTCH EDUCATION
IN GENERAL

Dewey's denial of absolute values, his insistence that learning which leads to growth must be based on the experience of the child, and that the aims of education must be to modify behavior rather than to impart knowledge—all this gives American education a transitory flavor and ties it closely to the society into which the child is to be fitted. It also provides an effective smoke screen preventing comparison of American education with that of countries having similar ways of life. Indeed, we have long lived in educational isolation and it is time we look around to see what is being done in other countries.

To get the necessary data is quite difficult—there seems to be no agency in the United States collecting such information. Through the great kindness of Mr. Philippe F. Scholten, LL.B. (University of Leyden), M.A. (Yale University), now residing at Woodbury, Connecticut, I have been able to obtain rather full information on the Dutch school system, including the complete curriculum for 1957–58 of a representative secondary school.[1]

First, a brief word on education in general in Holland:

The 11 million Netherlanders have six universities besides several university-level higher institutions. At the end of this

[1] Mr. Scholten did far more than collect information from Holland. He translated, tabulated the curricula, answered long lists of questions, and checked my understanding of the facts. For the manner in which I have presented this material, he must not be held responsible. I do not know Mr. Scholten personally. He wrote me commenting on one of my speeches and had such interesting things to say about Dutch education that I immediately seized upon him and have since imposed shamelessly on his kindness and unselfish concern for American education. On the strength of his personal experience with European and American education he has made himself into something of an expert on comparative education. I am deeply grateful to Mr. Scholten for having so generously given his special knowledge to this appendix on Dutch education.

229

résumé a number of charts will be found giving detailed information about the Dutch educational system. The Dutch system resembles that of most continental European countries, in so far as the competence of its secondary-school graduates at age eighteen is concerned, though it has a six-plus-five or six-plus-six system; that is six years of common elementary school and five or six years of separate-tracks secondary school. In France the secondary track is seven years, in Austria eight, in Germany nine, and so on. These are administrative details. The Dutch system lends itself best to comparison with ours because of our own six-three-three system. Education in continental Europe has always been surprisingly equal in quality as well as similar in form and in the details of curricula, the unifying factor being the traditional demand of European students to have access to the universities throughout the continent. The universities themselves have always had fairly uniform standards. These go back to the unity of Europe in the Middle Ages under a universal church which was the educator of the people.

In Holland, education from kindergarten to university is almost entirely financed by the government. The six-year elementary schools are free; the secondary schools charge small fees which are adjusted to family finances, and university fees average about seventy-five dollars per year.

Dutch elementary education began in the mid-eighteenth century. As long ago as the early years of the nineteenth century her grade schools were considered among the best of Europe. As is the case with the other smaller democracies—Switzerland, the Scandinavian countries, etc.—elementary education is particularly good, reflecting democratic desire to equip every child with a good basic education. Pupils are ahead of those in our elementary schools from the first year onward.

All Dutch children go through six elementary grades. The least able continue in elementary school for two more years; the others have six choices. Two of these are continuation schools which are terminal schools and preclude careers in the "professions." Graduates of the third have very limited access to university courses. The other three are academic secondary schools.

Admittance to the academic secondary schools is by examination. The elementary teacher advises parents whether or not their children are likely to succeed in these schools and his advice is usually taken. The children who attempt the examinations are therefore already a select group and 80 per cent pass. There are always opportunities for "late-blooming" children to switch to a higher secondary school if they develop unsuspected capabilities. Of course, this does mean a certain loss of time for no one is promoted in Holland—or anywhere in Europe—who has not demonstrated he is ready for the next grade. Elementary teachers themselves have had an excellent education and are of above-average intelligence. It is for this reason and because of the care they devote to assessing each child's potentialities that the teachers, in effect, select the children who go to the upper-track secondary schools. It is selection by merit, but it is also democratic selection, for parental poverty does not preclude a child from advancing to higher learning.

All but the most unintelligent students advance from elementary school into one of the following continuation schools:

(1) The trade school which lasts four years and compares favorably with our better vocational high schools.

(2) The advanced elementary school which also lasts four years and which offers a program not inferior to that of most of our high schools. During these four years the students study Dutch and French every year (though not every school day), English and German for three years; in mathematics they go as far as geometry and algebra; they have some physics and biology each year, but no chemistry. History includes general history of the world and Dutch history. They graduate at the end of their fifteenth year.

(3) And, finally, the secondary school Type "A" which lasts five years and which may be compared to our better public high schools.

In addition to these three *nonacademic* secondary schools there are also three *academic* secondary schools. One, the secondary school Type "B," lasts five years, and its graduates are qualified to study medicine and technical subjects at institutions of university rank, but not law or theology. The second is the Latin-grammar school Type "A" which emphasizes the humanities; the third is the Latin-grammar school Type "B" which emphasizes science and mathematics. Both of these Latin-grammar schools last six years and their graduates may study any subject at the universities. These academic secondary schools terminate with a long and comprehensive government-supervised examination covering all major subjects of the entire school program. This is the

usual European secondary-school-leaving examination. There are
no multiple-choice questions! I have appended an actual sample
of an essay in English to give an idea of the rigor of this examination.

During the five to six years the student spends in the academic
schools he is expected to read, in the original, ten major classics
in each of the foreign languages on his program, as well as
twenty-four major Dutch works for his Dutch classes. In mathematics, familiarity with differential and integral calculus, analytic
geometry, application of mathematics to physics, and spherical
trigonometry are required of all taking the mathematics-science
course. Those in the classical section are not far behind them in
mathematics and sciences.

I have made some calculations to compare the curricula of the
Dutch secondary schools with our own six-year junior-senior high
schools. The Dutch school day is 10 per cent longer than ours; the
school week lasts six days, or 20 per cent longer; the school year
lasts 240 days, or 33 per cent longer. The Dutch class period is 50
minutes and the homework required is two to six hours daily.
Further, except for gym, art, and music, only academic subjects
are taught.

I have attempted a comparison between two Dutch secondary
schools and our usual college-preparatory junior-senior high-
school program. As far as I can determine, our students must take
16 points of solid academic subjects in the four years of high
school, or four points per year, and these 16 points are all that are
required to enter college. If we were to give equal weight to the
first two years of our junior-senior high schools, the student ends
up with a total of 24 credit points in academic subjects for six
years—this is more than is usually required. The Dutch student
ends up with 30 credit points for the five-year school. For the
six-year school he ends up with 40 points, or 66 per cent more
than we.

To give you an idea of how these credits are obtained, let me
run down the figures for two of these secondary schools:

First, the five-year secondary school "A": 4½ points for the
mother tongue (Dutch); 10½ points for three modern languages:
French, English, and German; 3 points for history and political
science; 4 points for economics and accounting; geography, 2½
points; mathematics, 3 points; physics, chemistry, and biology, 3
points. I think you will agree that by the end of his sixteenth

year the Dutch student at a five-year school such as this *nonaca-demic* secondary school is at least well versed in basic subjects as the American college freshman. Even so, he will be admitted to only a few courses at a university since he is really not considered to be an "academically educated" person!

Now as to the six-year academic Latin-grammar school. Let us take Type "B," the one which specializes in mathematics and science, since it is closer to American education than the purely classical one: the mother tongue (Dutch), 4 points; the usual three modern languages, 8½ points; Latin and Greek, 11 points; history, 3 points; geography, 2 points; mathematics, 5½ points; physics, chemistry, and biology, 6 points.

These school programs are of course tailored to fit a small country with a language not spoken elsewhere; also a commercial country with large overseas interests. Foreign languages, therefore, occupy an exceptionally important place in the curriculum. If we in this country attempted a curriculum of equal solidity and breadth of knowledge we would naturally limit ourselves to, say, two foreign languages and soften the rigor of the course, as do the larger European countries which teach one less foreign language but otherwise are on a level with the Dutch schools. Our high schools are not only inferior to the Dutch secondary schools in foreign languages but in all other subjects as well.

Two major educational surveys backed by vast sums of money and conducted by large staffs of researchers have been made recently in this country. I invite you to compare the Dutch program with the college-preparatory programs worked out in these studies and suggested as "ideals" to strive for in our high schools. When you hear the statement: "Our best schools are still unsurpassed in the world," I suggest you "look at the record."

We have needed less education than Europe because we have always had so much more land and resources relative to population than Europe has. But in the short time since we became an independent nation we have multiplied prodigiously and wasted much of our natural wealth. At our present growth rates our population density will equal that of Europe in eighty years. As we approach European conditions, we may find that we shall have to make a choice: educate our children better or downgrade our standard of living. We still have a margin of safety, but it is none too soon for all of us to think this matter over carefully.

If we have the wisdom to prepare in time for a future when as much will be demanded of our children in education as is currently the case in Europe, we might consider taking as a model the Dutch system or that of any one of the small democratic countries—perhaps the Scandinavian system. It would be absurd to claim that their education is better because it is "aristocratic." There is no way to explain it—it is just infinitely better than ours. "To prohibit us from the benefit of foreign light," warned Jefferson, "is to consign us to long darkness."

SUMMARY INFORMATION ON DUTCH SCHOOL SYSTEM

Free and Compulsory Elementary School (grades 1 to 6 attended by all children; least capable continue through grades 7 or 8 and then learn a trade).

Post-elementary School—following choices:

1. Trade School (grades 7 to 10)
2. Advanced Elementary School (grades 7 to 10)
   Curriculum approximates *average,* but *not* our best (United States) high schools.
3. Secondary School Division "A" (grades 7 to 11)
   Curriculum—See Chart I

(1 and 2 do not permit entrance to university; 3 does not permit enrollment in university except for courses in geography, sociology, and economics. Compares favorably with our *best* high schools.)

Higher secondary schools entitling graduates to enter universities:

Curricula—See Chart I
Week's program—See Charts II and III

4. Secondary School Division "B" (grades 7 to 11)
   (Graduates may study sciences and medicine at universities, but *not* theology or law.)
5. Latin-Grammar School Division "A" (grades 7 to 12)
   Stresses humanistic subjects
6. Latin-Grammar School Division "B" (grades 7 to 12)
   Stresses mathematics-science

May take any university course

7. Lyceum (grades 7 to 12) (term given a school which combines 5 and 6, or 3, 4, 5 and 6, as in sample school.)

University courses:

Holland (population about eleven million) has six universities, of which all but one (the newest) have the traditional five faculties. In historical order these are: theology, law, medicine, the humanities, and mathematics and the natural sciences (one university lacks the faculty of natural sciences). Teaching concentrates on scientific approach to learning; practical application plays secondary role. There are also several technical institutes of university rank.

Two professional degrees:

Candidaats corresponds to our M.A., after two to three years. It is not a proper degree or termination point of study, but marks end of subject studied rather broadly; thereafter more specialized study leading to:

Doctorandus degree after two to three years for which candidate is examined in his field of specialization where he must show a very deep and critical understanding; examination covers one major, several minors. A number of papers required and in general it corresponds to Ph.D. or final professional degree in United States.

There is also a *doctor's degree* for which we have nothing comparable. It is won, as a rule, by men who are already active in their professions in which, as *doctorandus*, they are already fully qualified. For doctor's degree a major thesis of original research must be submitted, but this degree bestows no further practical qualification (it is honorary and desired chiefly by university professors).

Special requirements for physicians:

1. After one year a preliminary examination (*propaedeutic*) covering *premedical* courses in advanced physics, chemistry, biology, etc.
2. Next usual *candidaats*—minimum two years, more often three.
3. Usual *doctorandus*—minimum two years, more often three.

4. One year study and internship followed by examination called *semi-arts*.
5. Another year study and internship followed by examination called *arts*. (Arts is Dutch word for physician.)

This last is a state examination, not a university examination, and makes physician a licensed doctor. The procedure is similar for licensed dentist, veterinarian, or pharmacist.

Unlike United States, where each state has its own regulations, all examinations are alike in Holland.

Special schools:

Besides the previously mentioned pre-university schools, there are special schools for:
1. Difficult but intelligent children.
2. Children with lower I.Q.'s.
3. Children with chronic diseases, or whose health chronically interferes with school attendance.
4. Experimental schools, work places, for an extraordinary school curriculum (electives, but these are *in addition* not in substitution of regular school courses).

All schools and universities must be approved by state, and all examinations, written or oral, are given by a Board of the Ministry of Education, Arts, and Sciences. None are multiple-choice questions.

There is no basic difference between public and private schools —all must have the same curriculum approved by state. Private schools in addition teach religion of their particular church. Cost of public and private schools paid by state—money for religious instruction donated by private organizations.

There is no *tuition for elementary schools*. For advanced elementary and secondary schools tuition fees are fixed according to the income of the family, varying from $10.00 to $60.00 per annum. University fees are similarly graduated—maximum being $75.00 per annum for first five years; thereafter university study is free.

Few scholarships, but interest-free loans are numerous—to be paid back within ten years after graduation.

Total cost at a Dutch university (including board, room, books, traveling, tuition fees, and incidentals) is about five hundred dollars per annum.

Technical subjects (including engineering) are not taught in universities, but at institutes with university rank (for engineering —Technical Institute of Delft). In addition, more institutes for other technical studies (agriculture, economics). Furthermore, architecture, fine arts, business, applied arts, music, social work each have one institute.

Secondary and Latin-Grammar Schools (General Information)

1. Schools are open six days a week. Older students have two hours each on two or three afternoons in addition to regular five morning classes. (Fifty minutes each class period)

2. Vacations:

Fall	4	
Christmas	15	
Easter	11	
Summer	48	
Total	78	vacation days.

   School year thus has about 240 school days.

3. Advanced Elementary and Trade School pupils attend school from twelfth to end of fifteenth year.

   Secondary School Division A and B from twelfth to end of sixteenth year.

   Latin-Grammar School from twelfth to end of seventeenth year.

4. Professional degrees: add from four to six years, i.e., to the end of the twenty-first or twenty-third year.

   Physicians, dentists, etc., will complete study and internship and obtain state license at the end of twenty-fourth to twenty-sixth year (depending on specialization, if any), after seven to nine years of medical education and internship.

5. Homework averages: Nothing for first three grades; one to two hours for next three grades (i.e., through Elementary School); two to six hours daily in pre-university secondary schools.

6. Grading system runs from one (very poor) to ten (excellent); all subjects must have at least six for average mark. If three subjects fall below four, grade must be repeated; if below five, the pupil is promoted on probation. (This is for the end-of-year examinations—these are state controlled and uniform.)

7. Drop-out figures—sample school has about five hundred pupils

and gives Secondary School A and B Latin-Grammar School
A and B program.

Graduated in 1957:

Latin-Grammar A   —all 12 pupils—academic courses

Latin-Grammar B   —   14 out of 17 (about 82 per cent)
                            pre-university academic courses

Secondary Division B— 21 out of 24 (about 87 per cent)
                            academic courses

Secondary Division A— 13 out of 15 (about 87 per cent)
                            academic but not pre-university
                            course

Of pupils completing seventh grade (which is taken by all
four above-mentioned divisions) 77 per cent graduated into
the eighth grade of Secondary School and 69 per cent into that
of Latin-Grammar School; 68 pupils completed eleventh grade.
Apparently from eighth to twelfth grade there was a total loss
of about 20 per cent.

Fifty-three passed final examination and were thus eligible to
enter university. This represents approximately a 50 per cent
drop out of those entering seventh grade. Only 30 per cent will
finish their university education—in general because of lack of
determination. Even so, their education has been so good that
they will be able to obtain excellent positions.

As an example of the kind of linguistic ability expected of
European secondary-school graduates I give below a typical
English test for the terminal examinations of our sample Dutch
school. In the larger European countries, the students must do
this sort of thing in at least two foreign languages; in Holland in
at least three. Compare this with the linguistic examination in
two languages for American candidates for the Ph.D. degree.
This is an actual 1957 Dutch test.

The Rise of European Civilisation

It is impossible to draw an abrupt line of division between one
period and another, above all in the history of so vast and complex
a process as the rise of a civilisation, and consequently the date which
I have chosen to mark the end of this "survey" is a matter of practical
convenience rather than of scientific definition. Nevertheless there is
no doubt that the eleventh century marks a decisive turning-point
in European history—the end of the Dark Ages and the emergence

of Western culture. The precious revivals of culture in the age of Justinian and that of Charlemagne had been partial and temporary, and they had been followed by periods of decline, each of which seemed to reduce Europe to a lower stage of barbarism and confusion than it had known before. But with the eleventh century a movement of progress begins which was to continue almost without intermission down to modern times. This movement shows itself in new forms of life in every field of social activity—in trade and civic life and political organisation, as well as in religion and art and letters. It laid the foundations of the modern world not only by the formation of that society of peoples which, more than any mere geographical unit, is what we know as Europe.

This new civilisation was, however, still far from embracing the whole of Europe, or even the whole of Western Europe. The culture that we regard as characteristically Western and European was confined in the main within the limits of the former Carolingian Empire, and found its centre in the old Frankish territories of Northern France and Western Germany.

Chart I

TOTAL CLASS PERIODS FOR ENTIRE COURSE

	SECONDARY SCHOOL A (Very limited access to university)	SECONDARY SCHOOL B (Mathematics-Science)	LATIN SCHOOL A (Human-istics)	LATIN SCHOOL B (Mathe-matics-Science)
	GRADES 7 to 11		GRADES 7 to 12	
Greek	..	..	29	21
Latin	..	..	37	28
Dutch	20	18	18	18
French	19	16	16	16
German	15	11	10	10
English	17	13	13	13
History	12	11	17	14
Political Science	3	1	..	..
Geography	12	11	9	9
Economics	4	1	..	..
Accounting	14	3	..	..
Mathematics	15	25	18	24
Theor. Mechanics	..	4	..	..
Physics	5	11	4	10
Chemistry	6	10	3	9
Biology	4	8	5	8
Cosmography (Astronomy)	..	1	..	..
Geom. Drawing	..	2	..	..
	146	146	179	180
Arts Painting } Minor Spanish Religion } Electives	21	22	27	27

Class Periods: 50 minutes
School Days: 6
Homework: 4 to 6 hours daily

Chart II

NUMBER OF CLASS PERIODS PER WEEK

SECONDARY SCHOOL A (*very limited* access to university)
SECONDARY SCHOOL B (enrollment in mathematics and science faculties of university permitted)

Grades 7 to 11	7	8A	B	9A	B	10A	B	11A	B
Monday	5	5	5	5	5	5	5	5	5
Tuesday	5	7	7	5	5	7	7	7	5
Wednesday	5	5	5	5	5	6	5	5	6
Thursday	7	7	7	7	7	6	7	6	7
Friday	5	5	5	7	7	6	7	7	7
Saturday	5	4	4	4	4	5	5	4	5
Total number of class periods per week	32	33	33	33	33	35	36	34	35
Total number of class periods for 1 year (40 6-day weeks—240 days)	1,280	1,320	1,320	1,320	1,320	1,400	1,440	1,360	1,400

SECONDARY SCHOOL B may study sciences and medicine.
SECONDARY SCHOOL B may not study law or theology.

Chart III

NUMBER OF CLASS PERIODS PER WEEK

Latin-Grammar School (Graduates may take *any* university course)
A—Humanistic
B—Mathematics-Science

Grades 7 to 12	7	8A	B	9A	B	10A	B	11A	B	12A	B
Monday	5	5	5	5	5	5	5	5	5	5	5
Tuesday	5	5	5	7	7	7	7	7	7	6	6
Wednesday	5	5	5	5	5	5	5	5	5	5	5
Thursday	7	7	7	7	7	7	7	7	7	7	7
Friday	5	5	5	7	7	7	7	7	7	5	7
Saturday	5	5	5	4	4	4	4	4	4	5	4
Total number of class periods per week	32	32	32	35	35	35	35	35	35	33	34
Total number of class periods for 1 year (40 6-day weeks—240 days)	1,280	1,280	1,280	1,400	1,400	1,400	1,400	1,400	1,400	1,320	1,360

NOTE ON RUSSIAN EDUCATION

One consequence of the extreme sensitivity of American educationists to all criticism is that they have been slow to perceive the challenge of Russian education and even slower to admit the threat it represents to our country. In no other way can one explain the amazement and shock expressed by eminent educational leaders who finally went to Russia this year to check for themselves. As far back as 1954 people outside education had warned of the tremendous educational development in Russia and had urged that we put our own educational system in order. These warnings were airily dismissed as "hysterical" and the warners were told not to interfere in affairs about which they could know nothing—not having taken the prescribed credit courses in "education," one must presume! We hear a different tone now. "We were simply not prepared for the degree to which the U.S.S.R., as a nation, is committed to education as a means of national advancement," they say.

In the Office of Health, Education, and Welfare itself they have long had much material on Russian education; it was finally brought out in the report on "Education in the U.S.S.R." This material must have been available for at least three years, during which time many people spoke out worriedly on our growing shortages of trained man power which are a consequence of our inadequate public-school system—but not a single progressive educationist saw the danger. Even today these educationists try to disparage the Russian achievement and disclaim its significance for America because the Russians do not educate the "whole child," and thus no matter how much mathematics, or science, or foreign languages the Russian children learn, our children are still the best educated in the world. They are, after all, "life-adjusted." Much stress is also being laid on the narrowness of Russian education—its alleged overemphasis on mathematics and

243

sciences. We are solemnly warned to do nothing that would rob our children of their present wholesome and well-rounded education. All this is muddled with expressions of horror at the study load carried by Russian children and the evil purposes for which the Russian state educates them. Much is also made of the "aristocratic" nature of Russian education, and figures are wildly bandied about to prove how few Russian children actually graduate from the ten-year school or enter universities.

Should these alibis of our schoolmen be widely believed, we might well falter in our present momentum toward actively upgrading American education. It may, therefore, be helpful if the American parent be given the facts as we are able to obtain them. Of course, as Winston Churchill said, Russia still "is a riddle wrapped in a mystery inside an enigma," and we cannot be certain we have the correct information about everything that goes on there. Many competent persons have visited Russia lately, inspected her schools and universities, and reported on them. A number of scholarly papers and books have been published. It is better we err by overestimating her school system than by underestimating it. Above all, we cannot afford not to know the essentials about this system for it produces extremely efficient graduates, ready to be assigned by the government to any position where they can effectively carry out their ruler's policies and objectives. By last reports, many Russian medical students are simultaneously learning one of the Asian languages; presumably they will—like missionaries—spend their lives in some hot and unhealthy country, proselytizing for the Marxist faith, or rather for Russian imperialism, by winning the gratitude of native patients. Have we anything in this country to match the effect of such a program?

We cannot be satisfied merely to match the Russian educational system for we must have citizens who are not chessmen to be moved to position by their masters. If we are to hold the Soviets at bay and still remain a free democracy, we must have citizens who are, every one of them, better human beings as well as more competent workers in their field.

Nor would it be wise to allow ourselves to be lulled into a premature sense of security by recent reports of Khrushchev's heavy-handed meddling with Russian education. No more welcome news for us has come out of Russia in some time than the reports of the new Khrushchev educational policy, first announced July

14, 1958, and later amplified in his memorandum of September 20, 1958. The reforms proposed by Khrushchev would make Russian secondary and higher education more selective and hence more competitive. For the majority of Russia's children, schooling after age fifteen would alternate with factory or farm work. There is no evidence that educational standards would be lowered. The objective appears to be to bring education more closely into line with the requirements of the Russian state and to avoid producing intellectuals for whom there are no jobs available. It may be that Russia's rulers have found an educated public more difficult to handle than they expected. Many Western experts have been hoping this would happen. However, policies can change overnight in Russia. Demanding that the least talented students interrupt their studies for periods of practical work does not in itself lower the quality of Russian education. It merely postpones the time when the average student is finished with schooling. Should the need arise, these interruptions could be stopped with a stroke of the pen. It would, therefore, be most unfortunate if we took a shift in policy of this kind too seriously, and if it were used to reinforce the claims made by our educationists. Let me explain a little about these claims.

First, as to the claim that we educate the "whole child." This is exactly part of what is wrong with our schools. They attempt to do too many things which could be done elsewhere. Consequently, they fail to do the proper job of formal education. A child's home and church develop in him manners, personality, good character, and devotion to ethical and religious principles. A good school will reinforce these characteristics and, in addition, develop self-discipline, orderly habits of thinking, respect for facts, contempt for unsupported slogans and clichés, and the ability to handle abstract concepts and ideas. Can we say that our schools accomplish this?

Second, as to the narrowness of Russian education: It is well to note that in its report on "Education in the U.S.S.R.," the highest agency of United States education, the United States Department of Health, Welfare, and Education gives the percentage of time allotted in the ten-year schools as 46.9 per cent for the humanities (Russian language and literature, history, geography, foreign languages, and .3 per cent to the constitution of their country) and 42.4 per cent for sciences and related technical training! Several surveys have been made in this country to test the historical and geographical knowledge of high-school graduates and of college students; all show widespread ignorance. In foreign languages we cannot match the Russians who are *all* learning at least one foreign language. Visiting American engineers report that all their opposite numbers are able to speak either English, German, or French, and to read technical papers in all three languages. They also report wide reading of Russian and foreign classical literature—often in the original—among technical people. Our children do not now get an education which develops the mental part of the "whole child" adequately.

Third, the study load of Russian children is indeed heavy but not significantly heavier than that carried for generations by European children aspiring to higher positions in life. What makes the Russian system so formidable is that *so many more* of her children obtain this higher type of education. Russia, therefore, has a much larger reservoir of people with a good general education from which to select the most talented for further professional training. She can, therefore, set her admission standards to the institutions of university rank higher than we can. There are some three times as many eager aspirants than there are places in these institutions; more significantly, there are more of these places than are needed by Russia so she has a surplus to export to the underdeveloped countries which we cannot match since here we have in fact a deficit of well-qualified professional people.

Fourth, the usual alibi for the poor quality of American public education, that abroad they educate the classes and here the masses, is now—believe it or not—being applied to Russia! The alleged fact that only a small number of youngsters graduate from the ten-year school is deplored by many educationists. But, as I pointed out in Chapter 8 of this book, our retention figure for high-school students is currently 55 per cent (that is of 100 entering the fifth grade of 55 graduate high school) of whom about 25 per cent enter college (*Statistical Abstract of the United States, 1957*), whereas apparently some 39 per cent of Russian children complete the tenth grade and 35 per cent graduate. It must be remembered that every one of these graduates has had a rigorous college-preparatory course and that those who dropped out earlier have gone on to various other schools of a vocational nature. In comparing dropout figures, it is necessary to take into consideration that at seventeen the Russian student is about at our college sophomore level.

In his work on *Soviet Education for Science and Technology* Korol attempts to evaluate how much the Russian ten-year school graduate must know to pass the secondary-school-leaving examination. It may be said at once that he needs to know less than students taking similar examinations in other European countries who have had twelve to thirteen years of schooling. Even so, the standard of the Russian examination is very high. Korol takes two out of a considerable range of subjects in which the Russian student is examined—algebra and physics—and compares them with the level of our College Board Achievement Tests in these subjects. Of the minority of high-school graduates who go to college, only a relatively small percentage take the College Board Achievement Tests. Many state universities do not require any admittance test; many private colleges merely require Scholastic Aptitude Tests which measure the native ability, not the actual scholastic achievements, of the student.

Comparison is difficult because of the different methods used in testing the student. Nevertheless, careful examination of all the evidence available shows that *"in topic coverage in algebra the Russian examination involved is roughly equivalent to the College Board Advanced Mathematics Examination"* (Alexander Korol, *Soviet Education for Science and Technology*, page 435). Only about 10 per cent of American high-school graduates (among them are many graduates of private college-preparatory schools which cuts down the percentage from the *public* schools) take the mathematics courses on which the *Advanced* Mathematics Examination is based and not all of them actually take the Advanced Mathematics Achievement Test. But 35 per cent of Russian children entering the fifth grade end up passing the algebra examination which is comparable to our Advanced Mathematics Examination. And, finally, to make this sad tale still worse, many American high-school graduates who are admitted to college—even those majoring in science or engineering—*"have deficiencies in beginning algebra and plane geometry"* (*ibid.*, page 435). We do not know how well Russian students use what they have learned at school, but we know that they are exposed to far more and higher mathematics than our children.

The comparison in physics is more difficult because of different emphasis here and in Russia on the various branches of physics. It was found that of the 148 topics appearing in the Russian examination only 32, or 22 *per cent, are taught in American high schools* (*ibid.*, page 445). In general, the Russian level of knowledge was compared with that required in the College Board *Advanced* Placement Test. "Students taking this examination have had an accelerated program in physics in high school and hope to score high enough to be permitted to obtain credit for first-year [college] physics" (*ibid.*, page 440). As of 1955, the Advanced Placement Test was just becoming known and the number of candidates was only *1 to 2 per cent* of those who took the Achievement Test (*ibid.*, page 440).

Apart from the fact that all 35 per cent of Russian children entering the fifth grade pass these difficult secondary-school-leaving examinations and that they have all had more algebra and physics than the tiniest fraction of American high-school graduates, it must be remembered that American students take only three achievement tests if they take any at all. They can, therefore, choose the subjects in which they excel and on which they have concentrated. Russian students must take many more subjects in their final examinations and these are all on about as high a level as algebra and physics.

We have had one hundred years of universal education; the Russians only forty years of which the first fifteen had to be written off as a dead loss. We are still, in general, technologically ahead of them but not in every field. As Professor William A. Nash of the College of Engineering of the University of Florida writes about a related matter in a manuscript (which I hope he will publish soon), "we did not find the highest level of basic research in the field of mechanics to be any better in the Soviet Union than in the United States. However, the *quantity* of this high-level work in the Soviet Union *is now between two and three times that in America*, with the almost certain expectation that the Soviet endeavor will increase rapidly (as evidenced by the large number of students who are currently undergraduates and beginning graduate students) to such a point that *within five to ten years from now their efforts will perhaps be of the order of ten times our present effort*. Unfortunately, the current indications are that our research effort during that period will increase only by a very modest amount."

Professor Nash (who reads Russian) went with two other Americans to visit the Academy of Sciences of the U.S.S.R. last year.

He had received a personal invitation and the trip was sponsored by the National Academy of Sciences, Washington, D.C. The group toured Russia for twenty days and inspected nine major institutes of university rank. They were among the few Americans who have had the opportunity and time to study in detail the dissertations submitted by the Soviet students for "candidate" and "doctoral" degrees, and they were the first men since the late 1930's in the field of theoretical and applied mechanics to be allowed to visit Soviet laboratories doing research in this field. The sentences quoted above sum up the Russian threat throughout education: mass education of highest caliber and at an accelerating rate. This is the challenge we face.

The fact that Russia educates her people to serve the purposes of a totalitarian state and uses them with little consideration for their personal preferences is irrelevant to the question of how well she teaches them the subjects needed by everyone in this age of technology. The more ruthlessly Russia uses her man power, the greater the danger to us, for we must persuade where she can command. Let us not underestimate an opponent because we reject his political means and goals. The more these endanger our freedom, the greater our need to outdo him in the quality of our people. This means for each and every one of our children the best possible education we can devise. Let nothing and nobody stand in the way of this vital national objective.